Susanna Carolusson

BRAIN TRAUMA, PSYCHOSIS AND A MEANINGFUL LIFE

Being present

Published by Recito Förlag
Printed by Bording i Borås 2012

ISBN 978-91-7517-267-5

Bokutgivning.se
forlag@bokutgivning.se
www.bokutgivning.se

Recito Förlag AB
info@recito.se
www.recito.se

First edition
First printing

Translation: John Shelton
Original title: Det finns någon närvarande, *Recito Förlag*
Cover picture: Tobias Carolusson
Typesetting and layout: Malin Lindman

*Brain trauma, psychosis and a meaningful life:
Being present*

THANKS

I would like to thank psychologists Sigvard Lingh and Alf Nilsson, professor emeritus; occupational therapist and Director, Rune Johansson; and mother, choreographer and writer, Ami Skånberg Dahlstedt. You have reviewed my manuscript, given me tips about further references, encouraged me and drawn attention to ambiguities and inconsistencies in the form of the language, helped me see when psychological terms have been in need of an explanation and asked for clarification when I was too sparing with words. Rather like hawks, you have all helped to find the smallest mistakes in punctuation, which I would otherwise have missed. This, in turn, would have irritated me when the book was finally in print.

Thank you, Tobias, for teaching me to live intensively in the present, and for teaching me how to communicate, not only verbally, but in other ways, too. Thank you for showing that integrity and dignity can be maintained despite a loss of independence. Thanks Mårten, as the supervisor, you have dealt with the assistance of your brother with care, fairness and dependability. I also really value the natural way in which both you and Pia have treated Tobias with respect, humour, understanding and esteem. Thank you, Tore, my husband, for always putting the family first, for standing with your feet firmly on the ground through all of Tobias' fluctuations, and for the way in which you have supported me, often with humour, when I have needed it.

References and footnotes

I make use of reference parentheses, as is usual in academic texts, and footnotes. I supply the references after every chapter, so that it is easy to find the source of the experiences and opinions of others.

In cases where I have only aimed at explaining the meaning of a concept, I have sometimes chosen to make use of footnotes. This has been done in those cases where I feel that the explanation would obstruct a flowing text.

PREFACE

One day towards the end of August, I received a mail from Susanna. She asked if I was willing to write a preface to a book she was about to finish. Among other things in my reply, I wrote: «To my knowledge we have never met … but send me your manuscript.»

Well into the book, I find myself reading the manuscript from two mental levels simultaneously. One is as an «innocent» reader with no professional filter between text and reading. On the other level, I read as the supervisor I used to be, reading my students' dissertation manuscripts. As the «innocent» reader, I perceive a narration about the brain-traumatised Tobias, Susanna's son, and his family. They struggle patiently and unfailingly together to maintain the contours of everyday life. It is a gripping story that evokes turbulent feelings. I eagerly continue reading the fluent and engaging text in order to know more about Tobias' proceedings.

Now the professional in me takes over. First, I go back to the vicissitudes of the late 1960's and early 1970's. Along with the revolutionary spirit of that time, academic psychology received a vitalizing injection that opened up new horizons; a deepening and a widening of the subject. There was a strong repudiation of diluted and mossy behaviourism. My guiding-star was a profound and dynamic psychology that also took into consideration affects, relations, and advanced functions, such as cognition and language. My vision was a psychology that would be accessible to ordinary people, and an asset in everyday life.

Now it is October 2010. Twilight reigns. Contemporary catch-words are: cognitive science, CBT, internet therapy, coaching, positive thinking … Brain research has become a guide to psychology – instead of vice versa.

Tobias is severely damaged in his left cerebral hemisphere, which is the part of the brain that ultimately regulates cognition and language. In addition to paralysis in the right side of the body – now, fourteen years after the accident, considerably mitigated by exercise and family support –Tobias is afflicted with a severe aphasia. Right hemisphere damage is of secondary nature, if any. Modern brain research shows that the right hemisphere is involved in the regulation of: attachment, facial expressions of affect, speech prosody and the exchange of information through mutual eye contact. We do not know if or how Tobias' left hemispheric injuries influence those functions that are primarily connected to the right hemisphere. As evident from this book, we know that, after the accident, Tobias suffers from epileptic seizures and deep regressions with psychotic breaches. My own theoretical reflections reach out to see the congenital reflexes, action and cognitive operations as one branch of psychological development; and the inherited affects, relations and images as the other. And between these developmental lines, a constant exchange continues. In this perspective, the author's portrayal of the family's relations with Tobias becomes a close and heuristically vital testimony about how these developmental proceedings form a mental entity. It is also striking how Tobias, as an affective and relating person, somehow has access to all his developmental stages and ages. And that he struggles vehemently to allow them to be expressed right through the dead-locks of cognition and language.

The author is a qualified clinical psychologist and psychotherapist. Of course, this gives zest to Susanna's and the whole family's way of being with Tobias. Her story about the fourteen years after the accident, how the family hovers between hope when they see improvements, and despair when he regresses into psychosis, is not only touching. It is also of professional value. Psychologists and psychotherapists, ir-

8

respective of specialization, can read the book as a revealing documentation of the human being's function all the way down in the deepest psychological layers. But the author's language is also an invitation to health and care staff that has to deal with brain injured people in various ways, as well as those working with patients suffering from severe problems of a psychotic nature. I also recommend the book to each and everyone who is interested in learning about the life of someone unluckily stricken, like Tobias.

Alf Nilsson
Professor emeritus of clinical psychology,
Lic psychologist and lic psychotherapist

CONTENTS

INTRODUCTION

There are a number of reasons why I have written this book. Many readers of my earlier book about our son, Tobias, and his acquired brain injury (Carolusson, 2002) have made it plain that they wanted another book. They are longing for a sequel. That book described four years of Tobias' life after his very severe head injury and has been acknowledged as a strong, deeply moving and at the same time hopeful book about dedication and patience. Neurologist, Bertil Rydenhag, who wrote the book's afterword, said that then, in 2001, there was a lack of books that describe such a long process as four years. 15 years have now passed since the year zero in the Carolussons' personal chronology.

Why a book just now? My answer is that, in addition to the above mentioned desire, there is a need for a psychologically-oriented supplement to the neurological and pedagogical advancement of knowledge that dominates those publications that I have managed to find. The significance of knowledge about the language of the unconscious, the importance of understanding, the psychology of suffering, the power of patience, the art of dealing with people, as well as the strength of involvement and love all need to be discussed and contemplated to a much greater extent than is the case at present. Even now, 2011, fifteen years after Tobias' accident, the biological medical approach still dominates research and clinical care.

As I said above, there are very few publications concerning the psychological consequences of an acquired brain injury. When I search the literature, I do find a number of realistic and gripping texts about attitudes and responses in the journal

«Föräldrakraft», but this journal is mostly aimed at families with children born with a disability. The families of someone who has been injured as an adult will be hard put to find texts that can act as sources of inspiration when dealing with deeper psychological and existential questions.

When the dream and visions of a normal future for one's child, her leaving home and building a life of her own, is shattered, a sense of endless loss strikes one. It has no end. My previous book dealt with this subject far more than this book will, so I will only refer to the subject of family sorrow shortly here. Florian and Katz found that parents who were forced to look after their child during a phase when one would expect her to break free and move from home react in two ways: they reactivate their feelings of parental care and of having a meaningful objective, while at the same time, they feel sorrow over the fact that they cannot look forward to the freedom from child care that their peers can expect when their children leave the nest (Florian & Katz, 1991).

Perlesz and colleagues have published a report in which the authors state that relatives can seldom express what it is that they have lost, and that there are no theoretical models about this kind of loss (Perlesz et al, 1992). During a period after 1992, research was concentrated upon the stress and the burden carried by family member carers.

When, in December 2001, I published my book «There is someone in there», there were not many publications about the loss and grief that is suffered when a loved one, ones' own child in particular, suffers a brain injury. That same year, Perlesz and Rycroft published an article where it was shown that relatives experienced that they could not mourn because of the fact that society doesn't accept the existence, or underestimates the depth of this kind of sorrow. Relatives exemplified this with examples such as that they could be told: «You must be glad he / she survived» and «you must be strong for her / him now» (Rycroft and Perlesz, 2001).

Collings interviewed a group of five parents in Australia, whose child had suffered a brain injury in late adolescence or in early adulthood. The aim of her research was to answer the question: Do parents, whose semi-grownup child misses out on a normal development, feel sorrow? And: How does this sorrow express itself? She found that after the first phase of unreality, sadness, anger, guilt, physical disorders, depression, anxiety and difficulties in coping with everyday life, they continued to feel unending grief (Collings, 2008). Unending grief is not particularly acceptable in our society. One is expected to have a «year of mourning» or to enter into the final stage of mourning, the reorientation phase, according to Cullberg's crisis model (Cullberg, 2006). Cullberg's model can be applied to this situation, but only if one takes into account the fact that the relatives will switch between different phases, and that their unending loss means that they will never leave any phase behind them for good.

In my roles, as parent, teacher and supervisor, I have realized that people with an acquired brain injury suffer from both trauma and sorrow. A psychological trauma can be defined as injuries from an extremely harassing infringement, an event that is sometimes threatens life, and which is impossible to cope with mentally and emotionally in the current situation. The fact that an acquired brain injury is often associated with a traumatic event, a near-death experience with so called post traumatic stress symptoms (symptoms from a mental trauma in the past that cause continuous problems) has been mentioned here and there in articles, but I have been unable to find a publication that puts forward the possibility of treating the trauma of people with an acquired brain injury, psychologically.

During the years between publishing my previous book and writing the manuscript for this one, 2002 to 2010, I have supervised staff groups within daily care and assistants to people that come under the category of «acquired brain injury with cognitive disabilities». I have noticed that the training that is offered to staff usually concentrates upon pedagogical and supportive contributions with the focus on the physical disabilities, or difficulties with remembering and planning. Whenever psychological training is provided, it involves various forms of resource-focused and supportive contributions, such as «solution-focused» or «cognitive» treatment. Experts state things, often without any kind of explanation. For instance, they state that cognitive rehabilitation should be supportive, but should preferably not encourage insight. Why? How? And; Can one see things in a different light? are questions that are not raised. These popular models leave little room for suffering as a phenomenon. I get the impression that suffering is avoided. However, since suffering is a reality in every injured person's life, this avoidance leaves the patient alone with her existential reality, which is repressed. Such defences consume energy and strength. I think that this leads to further suffering. On the other hand, to acknowledge suffering is often accompanied by a feeling of fellowship and relief. When suffering is not allowed to be expressed in fellowship, happiness will be difficult to find. Happiness, as we all have experienced, facilitates learning and development. Staff, whose work is difficult and heavy, also need help to keep their spirits up.

However, if a cheerful manner is a criterion for the job, it will be a half-measure in my opinion. When happiness turns out to be gaiety, jargon and protection that hide an inability to get involved, then it feels contrived and dissociative. Health care and social services need people who can handle all kinds of feelings. This is a theme of this book – to be able to be touched, involved and inspired by both happiness and sorrow.

No one feels well after a trauma and I believe that everyone needs some form of help to understand and deal with it. Staffs suffer when there is no one to explain the sometimes strange reactions of the sufferers. There is far too little emphasis put upon the fact that care staff and social workers can make use of empathy[1] when talking to supervisors and to their teams in order to find inspiration for the understanding of the patients'/clients' behaviour.

When I supervise groups of staff, I am often the first person they have met who helps them understand the enormous contribution they would make if they can respect and put words to the suffering of their clients/patients. This is another reason why I am writing this book.

Individuals from Group 2[2] are often treated as if their brains are the cause of all behaviour that falls outside what is seen as being normal and preferable.

One example of this is the approach to epilepsy. Many people with brain damage have epileptic seizures. The epilepsy produces hyperactivity in certain areas of the brain. Thus, this hyperactivity is suppressed by medication. This is the bio-reductive logic. The cause is organic after all. As the reader will see, I shall give many examples of the fact that the biological cause is somewhat unimportant when it comes to understanding feelings. Individuals who remain not understood who are regarded as victims of biological processes and whose behaviour is regarded as lacking meaning become objectified, marginalized and deprived of a chance of maturing with their experiences.

Once again, Tobias has been generous enough to allow me to describe his suffering and his despair. He does it in the belief that the reader will realize that Tobias does as well as he can

---

1 The word «empathy» means compassion in everyday language. In the chapter called «The failure of short-term memory» I explain the concept from a psychological perspective.

2 The Law of Support and Service (LSS) to certain people with dysfunctions, covers three categories of dysfunction; «Group 2» are those who have acquired a cognitive impairment as adults, caused by brain trauma or illness.

and that he deserves respect for being who he is. To be seen, acknowledged and talked about as a person who has really tried, weighs up the shame he feels about his bizarre behaviour during his acute psychoses, some of which I have his permission to describe. The great contribution that he makes by giving me permission is to allow us to tell about how we have come to understand that psychoses can be understood, responded to and treated in the manner that psychodynamic psychotherapists have always claimed (and shown). Another fact that is illustrated by these examples of profound psychological commitment is that purely organic, i.e. the physical causes of the injury do not mean that the treatment must be unilaterally medical. Before his injury at 23 years old, Tobias was never anywhere near psychosis. So, there doesn't seem to be any hereditary or premorbid tendency towards psychosis. Neither did he show any symptoms that would suggest vulnerability from an early age as one might expect in many cases of psychosis in early adulthood. An injury the left hemisphere of the brain that is so severe that important language and logic centres are destroyed is a perfectly sufficient explanation. He cannot talk, he cannot think in sentences or understand abstract theories. He thinks mostly in images, he has feelings and he expresses himself by drawing in the air with a finger and through single words. Living in a world mostly made up of images is close to dream language, which in turn lies close to the language of psychosis. There are probably two reasons why Tobias has developed a tendency towards psychosis: the permanent damage to the left hemisphere following on the accident, and the post-traumatic stress resulting from such an incredibly difficult loss.

I imagine that many people can recognize themselves in this.

I am deeply motivated, in my role as psychologist and psychotherapist, to contribute with my professional knowledge of communication, commitment, empathy, integrity and of the importance of love. At the risk of being judged unprofessional, I will use the word «love». However, love is very difficult to define. It is a very subjective experience and the concept itself is more or less banned from the textbooks on professional therapeutic relations. Yet, I know that many of my colleagues have heard patients suggest that the therapist's love played a role in a successful treatment. I myself have been surprised when I have heard patients use the word when assessing their therapy with me. There have been, and maybe still are, professional interpreters of the role of love in psychological treatment. When I was a psychology student, 30 years ago, love was considered to be an essential healing illusion. It was in these terms that my teacher in the psychology programme talked about love. Whose interpretation should have precedence? If our commitment and warmth is felt by the patient as love, then let it be called that. The benefits of avoiding the word may be due to the risk of confusing erotic love with love for patients within a regulated treatment context and framework. I believe that love can be accommodated in a professional relationship, with the proviso that the therapist is free from or at least not steered by her own needs, or a need of being needed, in her treatment and responses. In order to make use of love without trespassing professional boundaries, the therapist must work unwaveringly with her self-knowledge. In an article in 2004, I wrote about the risks of perceiving all strong emotions that arise during treatment as having their source within the patient's problems. I wrote about the importance of developing good self-knowledge, through supervision and self-therapy, so that we can recognize our own needs and feelings. Otherwise we risk interpreting our own denied emotions as being those of the patients (Carolusson, 2004).

By analyzing and understanding what we feel about the patients, we will become more able to conduct ourselves professionally, in a way that is ethically sustainable and justifiable, in the long term.

If a course of therapy is to be considered scientific, one must have an academically acceptable theory about the cause of the problems, in order that the choice of treatment can be motivated by a suitable theory. I belong to the academic world. In my profession, I have followed and participated in the debate about mental illness, its causes and whether measures of treatment can be considered scientifically entrenched, well-tested and found to be effective.

Nevertheless, I see all too frequently that the causal analysis is hastily performed and that measures and methods of treatment are taken that lead nowhere because the first phase, a thorough review of the nature of the problem, was skipped over. Or, one starts a method of treatment that in fact leads somewhere, but theories as to why it produces results, how the changes were experienced by the patients, and how the patients experienced their role in the situation are missing. This is also the case when it comes to «proven effective» methods of treatment. So-called evidence in this case is that when one has managed to help a majority of a group of patents with the same diagnosis, hey presto! One draws the conclusion that the method can be recommended for everyone with this diagnosis. Clinically experienced therapists rarely work in this manner. In our philosophical and sociological theory of science studies, we are encouraged to think about the humanity and the values underlying the various theories and methods as well as the therapist's and the patient's subjective experiences of the nature of the achieved change.

There is a different approach to treatment within medicine and manual-based therapy. Symptoms and causes are lumped together with the result that the treatment of symptoms sometimes replaces a thorough examination or a causal analysis. Within health care, it is true that it is often necessary to mitigate potentially fatal symptoms before being able to investigate and resolve the causes. However, a lack of a holistic viewpoint has meant that the curing of symptoms has been awarded greater resources than explorative analysis. The pharmaceutical industry has almost certainly played its part in this development. Statistical correlations between the drug and symptomatic relief are «elegantly» documented, as one says using a scientific vocabulary. This medical approach has been transferred to psychotherapy, which is noticeable by the fact that public psychiatry demands a symptom diagnosis according to the DSM-system (DSM-IV, 1995), despite the fact that experienced psychologists and psychotherapists know that symptom diagnoses are of marginal importance when preparing the patient's unique plan and practice of treatment. This is a trend that entices therapists away from the earlier principle of taking a stance in questions concerning which treatment philosophy, ethics, and humanity should underlie the choices made in clinical practice. Many people may think that philosophy, etc., are ideological issues that get in the way of objective studies of treatment effects. That medical (pharmacological) research is a model of objectivity and control. Others are of the opinion that psychological treatment is so complicated that it cannot be studied in the same manner as pharmaceutical studies. It is true of course that psychological phenomena are difficult to study and psychosocial cause-effect variables impossible to control altogether, but even truly organic symptoms are influenced by psychological complexities, so a philosophical holistic science adds a lot, even to research in the medical disciplines. Behind every medical diagnosis and treatment is the underlying assumption about the difference between health and sickness, how sickness can be cured or relieved as well as how health can be achieved and maintained. Most broken bones are cured by surgical treatment; the bones are corrected and then held in place by plaster or other stabilizing materials. The cause is a break in the bone; the treatment is a surgical operation. This seems simple. In my world, as a psychologist, it is seldom so simple. I am sure that many doctors would agree with me that it is not so simple in their profession either, since medical research is more than just simple cause- effect correlations. A broken bone is a direct reason for an operation, but a broken bone can also be seen as a symptom. There can be underlying reasons for the broken bone that need to be rectified in order to avoid more broken bones: osteoporosis, abuse, accidental falls due to safety risks at work, cases of accidents where alcohol abuse is a contributing factor etc.

I will now use depression as an example of the complexity of psychology, as it is relevant in the case of brain injury. The reader who has no interest in academic discussions can jump forward to the paragraph starting «It is no coincidence that I mentioned depression» on page 8 (korrigeras in när texten är satt)

Patients diagnosed as having depression are treated with method X, and finally one has documented so many cases that one can make the conclusion that method X helps. What helped? X? If X helped – how did it help? Who cares?

We must care; we have an obligation to decide whether our methods help to create changes for the patient in a dignified manner. Does it increase the patient's sense of her own responsibility? Does the method help the patient to greater insight and to coping skills? Or was the patient intimidated to change, as in authoritarian parenting where the threat of punishment deters inappropriate behaviour? Intimidation techniques do indeed give results and may even provide evidence. In the 1970s, a behavioural therapeutic approach was sometimes used; one gave a painful electrical shock together with the smell, taste, and image of alcohol. The method was also tested in the treatment of undesirable sexual deviations and in the treatment of children who wet their beds. They had to sleep on an electric bed sheet that gave the child a shock when it peed on it and the dampness closed the circuit. These behaviour modifying methods were criticised for the very reason that they concentrated upon getting results and ignored the inner feelings of the patients. The critics held that questions of self-image, self esteem, morality and ethics should be taken into account in academic psychology and research. An academic debate ensued; can the inner world of people be studied at all and to what extent can intra-psychological phenomena be studied objectively? Is it necessary to be objective, and if not, how then can academic knowledge be accumulated? Hermeneutics and Existentialism already existed as academic options. Behavioural therapists, however, strenuously argued that since you cannot prove what's happening in the subjective inner world, let alone what happens in «the unconscious», an essential concept in psychodynamic theory and practice, then you have to put these questions to one side. Cognitive psychology then achieved a certain status among behavioural therapists, and one started to accept the study of thinking and attitudes. But «the unconscious» was, and to some extent still is, thought to be unscientifically vague and the psychoanalytic theories to be Freud's private imaginings. Behavioural therapists and neurophysiologists prefer to use the concept «non-conscious». As far as I understand the trends, cognitive behaviourists regard the word «unconscious» too speculative and based in psychoanalytical theory with such abstract concepts as «defence mechanisms», denial in particular. Psychologist Alf Nilsson, adamantly, and in my opinion, very convincingly insists that the concept of the unconscious plays an important role not only as «non conscious», but even in a structural functional sense. He draws an interesting parallel with the cognitive scientist, John Kihlstrom's assertion that explicit and implicit perceptions are neurologically based in two separate systems of perception. Like myself, Nilsson is a part of that generation who has studied and likes to refer to the importance of roots, by, for example, giving Freud the honour of having formulated ingenious models for the powers of the psyche's unconscious (Nilsson, 2009). I would like to add that Nilsson has been supported in his view by several neuro-psychoanalytically oriented researchers who make interesting connections between the unconscious and the brain's structural division into functions that have their origins in the various development stages in an evolutionary perspective (Solms & Turnbull, 2005), (MacLean, 1977), (Damasio, 1994/1999).

I sometimes make use of the concept «the subconscious» in my text. It is a habit I have from ordinary communication when working as a therapist. I make use of hypnosis, often with the aim of finding unconscious material that is of relevance to the therapy. When I address the patient's unconscious, I prefer to say «your subconscious». When I have a patient in a state of hypnosis, I, as the therapist, am more concretely metaphorical and visual in my language than I would be when talking to someone who is in an alert state of mind. «Subconscious» suggests that we are searching for something that is available, but lies a little deeper. When one induces hypnosis, one sometimes uses the word deep as in the suggestion to «go deeper into relaxation.» «Deep» and «Sub» are figurative expressions that can be easily visualized. Thus, I have found that the word is useful and practical. I cannot find the place where Jung made use of the expression, but it is rumoured that it was he that minted the concept «subconscious». I rather believe it was Pierre Janet.

I will now return to evidence and research concerning the results of treatment. An assumption within medical research is that if a certain statistical percentage of the patients are cured, then the method is effective. The question one must then ask is: Why weren't the rest of the patients cured? Were they «therapy-resistant»?

Yes, this awful word was used by The National Board of Health and Welfare in a preliminary version of their paper on the treatment of anxiety and depression in 2009. I cannot find this word in the final version, though (The National Board of

Health and Welfare, 2010). This is probably due to the massive criticism of the concept from psychotherapy organisations.

As an academician, one also needs to ask the question of what helps: Would method Y have worked just as well? Had another therapist using the same method produced the same results? Was it the feeling of being cared for, seen, understood, held and respected that activated the healing resources of the mind and body? Is the therapist's ability to create a trusting relationship more important than technique and method?

There is a well-cited, classical piece of research about the significance of being the subject of care, and that this feeling can be more important than the treatment itself. It is called «the Hawthorne effect» by Elton Mayo, Fritz Roethlisberger and William Dickson who studied workers at the Hawthorne factory in the Western Electric plant in Illinois between the years 1927-1932. They found that the employees experienced that the working conditions improved, when the lighting was both brighter and darker. Several similar experiments were performed with both changes and no changes to the environment, but in all cases the performance of the employees improved anyway. In all cases it was made clear that they were being given special attention. It was found that the workers appreciated the fact that the management was involved in their working environment, and that every change or even just the fact that observers were making notes was welcomed as a sign that the management cared. The original report is in Roethlisberger & Dickson *Management and the Worker*, from 1939, and referred to in a textbook on organization development (Robbins, 1979).

In evaluations of psychological treatment, similar psychosocial effects have been demonstrated. Patient-, therapist-, and other factors related to relationships are more important to the results of the treatment than the methods themselves. The therapeutic method has only a small influence upon the results (Wampold, 2001).

Anyone can see that a therapist that uses a proven, effective method can still cause damage if the therapist is insensitive, clumsy, arrogant, and a poor analyst. This is true even with a concrete medical practise such as surgery. The methods and tools are not sufficient in themselves, we know this. We will absolutely avoid a badly-trained, stressed, tired and uninterested surgeon. Therefore, effective methods are not enough. The patients need something more. This is true within psychological treatment as well. In the same way that we would not let our body be treated by an arrogant or careless surgeon, we would not expose our deepest feelings to a psychologist, doctor, or therapist who behaves in a manner that does not foster a feeling of trust. It is a question of response, security, and competence in psychological communication. Empathy is required if this competence is to be trustworthy.

This book deals with this question. It is important that questions like these are studied.

It is no coincidence that I mentioned depression as an example of how and what can be cured. There are numerous patients in medically-oriented health care that are depressed because of their life situation, or whose depressing life situation lowers their quality of life so that they develop symptoms of depression. This is especially true of people that have an acquired brain injury, have suffered a stroke or suffer from dementia. I have listened to lectures and conversations and read articles, all related to the health sector, in which injuries and illnesses of the brain are discussed as being the single cause of symptoms of depression. Psychological, emotional and relational causes are played down. This can be due to several things; lack of empathy, a one-sided biologically-oriented knowledge base, or the inability of patients to express their desire for psychological treatment, psychotherapy or at the very least a caring, empathic response that normalizes and provides an existential understanding of their depression.

In the same manner that a broken bone doesn't always reveal the underlying reason why the person was injured, the causes of depressions are seldom visible or obvious. The medical paradigm would have us believe that depression is caused by depression. Depression is a chemical disorder that doesn't need to be further explained. It just arises. From a biological perspective, depression is an imbalance of neurotransmitters or hormones. This, however, is not a cause and effect mechanism, it is a neurochemical correlate to a psychological experience. Medication that corrects the chemical imbalance hinders the neurochemical expression of the depression, which also alleviates the feeling of being depressed. The medicine cures the symptom, but if we haven't found out the causes of the symptoms then we do not understand what to do with the person in her life situation as a whole. In my opinion, we can't be content with the simple explanation that a chemical imbalance causes depression, even when the patient has a brain injury! Some brain injury specialists' opinions differ from mine; that the cause is in fact simple, the brain is damaged, it is injured and that this is exactly why the chemistry gets out of balance. They are not interested in deeper psychological causes. Maybe it's because they lack the skills to treat with psychological methods, with personal responsiveness, empathy and imagination? One cannot practise something one knows nothing about. One of the most accessible and factually compelling books I have read about depression as a normal reaction to loss is «The Healthy Depression» by Emmy Gut. She describes the necessary shielding during difficult periods of transition in life, and the importance of self-esteem if one is to avoid becoming depressed. Her arguments are based upon both psychodynamic and cognitive theory (Gut, 1990).

We don't stop a bear from hibernating but we become deeply afraid when someone becomes depressed. This is an interesting comparison. What would happen if we embraced the view that both depression and psychosis «are chosen» in anticipation of better times and a better situation? Better times can arrive if someone tries to understand and give sustenance to the person's self-esteem.

Self-esteem is the focal-point of all psychotherapy, no matter which tradition, so it ought to be natural that depressed patients get the chance to discover whether a psychologist or psychotherapist can strengthen their self-esteem before deciding whether a course of medication should be recommended.

I sincerely hope that my book will demonstrate the importance of responsive communication and a caring attitude between family members and their disabled relatives, between caregivers and clients and between therapists and patients.

REFERENCES

Carolusson, S. (2002) *Det finns någon därinne. Om vård, värde och värderingar vid förvärvad hjärnskada.* Lund: Studentlitteratur / Adlibris. Order from the author: www.carolussons.se

Carolusson, S. (2004) Självkännedom minskar risken för motöverföring. *Psykologtidningen, 15.*

Collings, Catherine. That's Not My Child Anymore! Parental Grief after Acquired Brain Injury (ABI): Incidence, Nature and Longevity. *British Journal of Social Work (2008)* 38, 1499–1517.

Cullberg, J. (2006) *Kris och Utveckling. Samt Katastrofpsykiatri och sena stressreaktioner.* Sthlm: Natur & Kultur.

Damasio, A. (1994/1999) *Descartes misstag. känsla, förnuft och den mänskliga hjärnan.* Sthlm: Natur & Kultur.

Gut, E. (1990) *Den sunda depressionen. Möjligheter och svårigheter i dess förlopp.* Wahlström & Widstrand.

Nilsson, A. (2009) *Det omedvetna i nya perspektiv. Ett psykiskt system mellan hudens och känslans beröring.* Sthlm: Brutus Östlings Bokförlag Symposion.

Robbins, S. (1979) *Organisational Behavior. Concepts and controversies.* New Jersey: Prentice-Hall Inc.

Socialstyrelsen. (2010) Nationella riktlinjer för depressionssjukdom och ångestsyndrom. http://www.socialstyrelsen.se/nationellariktlinjerfordepressionochangest

Solms, M. & Turnbull, O. (2005) *Hjärnan och den inre världen. En introduktion till psykoanalysens neurovetenskapliga grunder.* Sthlm: Natur & Kultur.

Wampold, B. E. (2001). *The great psychotherapy debate. Models, methods, and findings.* Mahwah, NJ: Lawrence Erlbaum.

THE CURRENT STATE OF KNOWLEDGE

There is a willingness among psychologically-oriented professionals to make us of non-verbal techniques in the rehabilitation and habilitation of patients with a brain injury. When words are lacking, as is the case with people with aphasia or other cognitive problems following a brain injury, non-verbal communication may be necessary. Physical therapists prescribe physical exercises; they will make use of touch in the form of tactile massage for example, and train body-awareness with a variety of methods. Speech therapists use pictures, symbols and signs. Psychologists make use of methods such as Art Therapy, mindfulness, hypnosis and mental training. I have found good examples of psychologists and psychotherapists who use hypnosis in rehabilitation after traumatic brain injury in general (Spellacy, 1992) and stroke in particular (Rossi, 2005). I mention hypnosis specifically since it is the oldest method of treatment in the west and has influenced many of the modern methods of therapy that are seen to be both effective and intensively curative.

Biologically-oriented research has always been well-funded. Stem cell research is a well-known example. By implanting correctly prepared stem cells from rats into a person's damaged brain, cells are converted into neurons, which in turn are converted into nerve tissue. However, we know too little about the results of operations of this type, so, until further notice, we have to rely on the research that shows that the brain spontaneously recreates neurons or dendrites. One of the foremost researchers in this area, Michael Nilsson, was interviewed in a newspaper along with his research colleague, Peter Eriksson. He says in the interview that «There is every reason to be cautious. There are fears that it might give rise to cancer. There is a risk that benign tumours will develop if the cells are not properly cleansed.» Scientists have also found that the brain only develops, heals and rehabilitates if it is stimulated, no matter whether a stem cell operation has been performed or not (Bohuslänningen, 2002). We parents and people with an acquired brain injury shouldn't have too high hopes about stem cell operations, for the next few decenniums at least. One person who is highly sceptical to stem cell operations is Arvid Carlsson who was interviewed by Ingrid Carlberg. She writes: «Arvid Carlsson thinks that is an absurd thought that new cells could grow and start functioning in the complicated mazes of the brain.» (Carlberg, 2008).

Even though most experts have claimed that damaged stem cells cannot be spontaneously repaired, there is now proof that stem cells rejuvenate, even without an operation. It would appear that both theories live side by side, and we can see practical proof of both of them. This might seem contradictory, but is there perhaps a logical explanation? Within stroke-rehabilitation, a number of researchers have noticed that psychosocial factors affect neurological healing more than was previously realized. The question is, how and under which circumstances.

Inherent spontaneous healing does not seem to exist in the brain cell's genome; it is rather that the right kind of stimulus is required. Doctor Mila Komitova, together with some colleagues, has written a treatise in which they disclose that rats that have had a stroke and subsequently treated with social contact and physical activity, recreated brain cells. Physical activity alone did not help, and it would seem that physical activity without a rich social environment could exacerbate the injury (Komitova et al, 2006). I have also found some promising studies about the training of cognitive functions in people. One such example is Hagberg van't Hooft's article about cognitive treatment for the training of attention and memory in children with acquired brain injuries (Hagberg-van't Hooft,

2005). Stimulation, training, methods of learning etc., are all very well, but one will never reach the patient herself if she is blind to her predicament. Imagining and wishfully longing to be the person one once was, and having those skills one once had but have lost, can drive a person into a world of fantasy where training and stimulation have no meaning. To escape a harsh reality in this way is not only protective, it also prevents development as well as requiring large amounts of energy, causing fatigue that in turn amplifies such symptoms as depression and confusion. One can perhaps be tempted to enter a stimulating environment such as music or nature, where there is nothing to remind one about one's disability (assuming that the experience of sound is intact). Listening to and making music, is used in rehabilitation and daily activities in order to stimulate healing after brain damage and the effect is scientifically documented (Schlaug, 2009). However, staffs involved in such activities sooner or later meet participants that at times refuse to take part or who can only participate in a sheltered context, not in everyday situations where their losses are painfully obvious.

The fact that people with an acquired brain injury are traumatised, with consequences on their behaviour and that insight, in combination with the supportive therapy, might prevent or alleviate decline or stagnation, is seldom discussed. There are few publications that describe how to help people with acquired brain injury to process their loss and to deal with their grief, especially if they behave in a manner that seems bizarre to others. A sympathetic exception is Bicknell, who, on the basis of a few case studies, describes how life within families with a child with a mental disability can be. I think this article is also relevant in the case of young adults with acquired brain injury since the author covers all aspects of life, including the part where the disabled person's parents age and die. Support will be needed, not only help to mourn the loved one, but even with other lost values, such as living environment and the secure routines that are a part of family life (Bicknell, 1982).

Hypnosis

In my earlier book, I described certain situations where hypnosis helped, both during narcosis and afterwards. Karen Johnson and her colleague, Errol Korn, have described a 16-year-old patient with an acquired brain injury who improved surprisingly well with the help of hypnosis and imagery. When she suffered from anxiety or depression, she could relieve her suffering with the use of hypnosis, which allowed her to imagine a safe place in which she played the piano (Johnson & Korn, 1986). Other examples of psychologists and psychotherapists who describe the use of hypnosis in rehabilitation after traumatic brain injury are Spellacy, in general (1992), and Rossi (2005), who deals with stroke in particular.

There is also documentation about the use of hypnosis under general anaesthesia and surgery. It has been shown that there is less bleeding (Meares, 1986/1999), the need for aftercare is lessened and both mental and physical recoveries are significantly improved. Björn Enqvist has done research on the use of hypnosis prior to jaw and chest operations and his results were significantly positive compared to the control group as regards pain-levels, bleeding and anxiety/calmness (Enqvist, 1997). Enqvist has also written about hypnotic communication in care and treatment (Enqvist, 2004) and on curative communication in health care (Enqvist & Bengtsson, 2005).

In a paper published in the journal «Hypnos», Spellacy discusses why hypnosis can be of use for patients with an acquired brain injury. Dysphasia, aphasia, attention deficit and cognitive difficulties can be efficiently dealt with by the experienced hypnotherapist and the author presents several of his own cases of how, in hypnosis, one always uses a simple vocabulary, a slow tempo, and an emotional intonation (Spellacy, 1992). This type of language can be generalised and used in all therapeutic communication with brain injured patients.

A group of psychologists at Eötvös Loránd University in Budapest have published an important book about health care and communication influenced by hypnosis (Varga, 2011). I have contributed with a chapter about the treatment of patients with a brain injury and their families. The book is about wordless communication and the value of suggestions within medical care. It has been written by internationally renowned psychologists and doctors competent in hypnosis. The focus of the book is upon communication and treatment. Most of the authors, of which I am one, are proficient in hypnosis, which we use more or less structured. Less structured means that the suggestive elements of hypnosis affect the communication technique, in the choice of words, the tempo and tone of voice.

The diagnosis and definition of psychosis

In contrast to my earlier book, which was about the role of the family, health care in the emergency and the follow-up phases, responses in everyday life, as well as the importance of love, this book's focus is upon the long-term battle between the acceptance of a new identity and a refusal to do so. A refusal to accept can take on a variety of forms depending upon the individual. However, through the insight my work has given me, I have come to realize that disorientation, depression, anxiety and avoidance are common reactions. In order to be able to create the stimulating environment that has been shown to further rehabilitation, health workers, teachers, assistants and relatives need to find meaningful channels for communication, even when the victim's inner world is in turmoil. This is especially true during states of crisis, as these are critical phases that have a bearing upon later developments. An insensitive, and for the sufferer, undignified response can cause iatrogenic injuries (injuries caused by health care workers, staff and treatment). When I read the the manual of psychiatric diagnoses, I find ample similarities in the cases of many of the brain-damaged people whose staff I have supervised, and in Tobias, with a number of the criteria required to be diagnosed as psychotic. Examples of symptoms of psychosis are: obsession, omnipotent beliefs, delusions, hallucinations, paranoia, belief that the food is poisoned, that symbols are attributed as being good or evil, insomnia, unnatural excitement, catatonia, obsession with ideas, etc. However, in the case of an organic injury, the psychosis diagnosis, according to DSM-IV, the most common manual for psychiatric diagnoses, is not considered to apply. Meanwhile, we know that it is quite possible to have a number of diagnoses, so why not both acquired brain injury and psychosis?

Strömgren (1964) has written about a state of psychosis, in the context of narcotics and solvents. He also wrote about psychosis after inflammation of the brain and the cerebral cortex, and after concussions or intracranial tumours. However, even though he apparently considered the diagnosis of psychosis justified in these cases, he did not go deeper into the psychological aspects of treatment.

In 1986-87, I worked at Falbygden Clinics, a psychiatric hospital for adults. We psychologists had special test batteries to assess the causes of memory- and concentrations-problems. A common group of patients at this time were painters with suspected solvent-caused brain injuries. All we did, however, was to work out the probabilities of there being a connection between solvent and injury so that the patients might possibly receive compensation for an occupational injury. Only a few of them proceeded with counselling in order to process their loss of cognitive functions and the changes that followed in their wake. We were not asked by our superiors to provide psychological treatment and I see this omission as a symptom of the fact that one underestimated the ability of people with a brain injury to recognize and process their loss.

The focus of this book lies with brain injuries that have arisen from a specific trauma or serious sickness and that have caused a dramatic deterioration of cognitive and perhaps even bodily functions. In my opinion, there is no cause to think that the brain injury alone, in a vacuum and unaffected by psychological and social influences, causes the psychotic symptoms. This is not in any way believable. I shall give a large number of examples below that the psychotic symptoms can be understood as a defence against the unbearable. My theory is that the brain injury is the major cause of the lack of higher defence mechanisms within the sufferer.[3] A person in harmony with a healthy brain makes use of defence mechanisms such as intellectualisation, rationalisation, repression, and sublimation. A damaged left hemisphere cannot make use of these kinds of defences. There will be a regression to a more primitive form of defence. Fragmentation, projection and projective identification are these primitive forms. Psycho-dynamic theories explain these defences so that they can be understood in terms of self-protection. They become evident in the forms of incomprehensible mania, omnipotence, an inability to discern the difference between concrete and symbolic actions and the inability to distinguish between inner and outer reality.

The well-known psychiatrist, Johan Cullberg, writes in his foreword to the Swedish translation of «Unimaginable Storms» that psychoses comprise a large group of psychiatric disorders, all of which may seriously impair the individual's contact with reality. They are often accompanied by confusion and disruption of the ability to think and perceive which can be expressed in delusions and hallucinatory experiences.» (Jackson & Williams, 1997).

---

3 Higher defence functions in psychoanalytic theory: the ability to make use of repression and sublimation. Repression means that a phenomenon can be kept away from consciousness, with ease and without having to deny its existence. Sublimation means that primitive (animal) sexual and aggressive forces or impulses, as they were called in early psychoanalytical literature, find expression in socially acceptable feelings, thoughts and activities.

Psychodynamically oriented literature

One might say that there is a dearth of literature and documentation that concerns itself with the depressive and psychotic periods that afflict people with brain injuries. In order to find like-minded psychologists with a depth of knowledge about psycho-dynamic phenomena, I had to search the general literature about psychoses that does not specifically deal with brain-injury. However, I did find many inspiring texts!

One such example is Sonja Levander. She describes in a book the great differences between health care units, and how some prefer a medication approach while others avoid medications, preferring psychological treatment. The use of «anti-psychotic medication varies a great deal between different hospitals and clinics. In certain places, a point is made of waiting with medication until after psychiatric contact in order to see what happens. Some go further and say that anti-psychotic medication is not necessary at all.» (p. 12)

«My job as a supervisor and psychologist at Soteria Nacka, a crisis and treatment centre outside Stockholm has in many ways convinced me that the psychological part of care is the vital part of the therapeutic process and is what makes it meaningful to the patient »(p. 16).

According to the psychodynamic approach, there is always an emotional stress involved: «The situation has been too difficult for the patient to cope.»

On the subject of medication, Levander writes: «In situations of confusion, it is too easy to simply deploy anti-psychotic medication, or raise the already existing dose, without wondering about what it was that may have affected the patient. One can have an attitude that says that the patient» had a new relapse, «which becomes an excuse for avoiding thinking about what has been the cause of the deterioration.» (Levander, 2007).

If one first and foremost sees psychosis as an organic disease, what then is one's attitude? The psychiatrist, Cecilia Brain (2007), took part in a day-long seminar about the discrimination of both patients and staff in psychiatric care. Admirably critical of the stigmatisation of schizophrenics and their relatives, Brain says that drug adherence is very important for schizophrenic patients. I quote her directly from the pamphlet that was published after this seminar. «You cannot take a break from medication because of the risk of a relapse and with each new relapse the prognosis worsens (...) I argue that it is a brain disease and that it is not due to the bad mother.»

It is noteworthy that a brain disorder is pitted against a narrow and simplified version of the psychoanalytic theory about insufficient security in the earliest phase of life, in a way that makes everyone in the audience want to lift this unnecessary burden of guilt from the shoulders of the mothers and to agree that the first option sounds better for all parties. However, the logic is weak. Reality is so much more complex: the low capacity of people with a psychosis depends both upon a brain injury or illness and a lack of self-esteem. To what extent this lack of self-esteem has its origins in the earliest years of life varies, naturally. Our lives are affected by an endless variety of events and relationships. To choose between two outdated options: mother or genes, as the cause of the problem, is not going to help. The loss of functions and independence, as well as a lowered quality of life, can be quite sufficient reasons for an outbreak of a psychosis. Anyway, I think it is important to understand, discuss and work with the lack of self-esteem and the perceived reasons for it, in an ongoing process of psychological and existential dialogue, protection, an honest response, stable relationships, taking an interest, etc.

Per Torell represented the parent perspective at the above mentioned seminar. He brought up the question of an important aspect of relationships that medication doesn't have any effect upon i.e. the psychotic person's abnormal ability to enter the private sphere. «People with schizophrenia or who are psychotic, for example, wander in and out of the personal and private sphere, making us confused, aggressive and irritable. They get too close, we can't manage that and it's noticeable. (...) There is only one way», claims Per Torell. «Get strategies, lots of strategies. Try constantly to understand and to analyse.»

«The frighteningly diffuse feeling of insecurity about who one is and what different events mean is probably one of the most agonizing things a human being can experience. The ground one stands upon starts to give way (...). The growing anxiety (...) is a feeling that in itself isn't psychotic. But it can start one off constructing a context of one's own, in order to avoid the anxiety-ridden chaos that a lack of control of one's own situation creates» (Wallin, 2008).

I would like to add that the very necessary strategies that Torell mentioned demand empathy, a good mental balance and self-knowledge if they are to work. The coming chapters illustrate this.

Levander explains the psychodynamic therapist's basic attitude. «Everyone who works clinically knows that different patients need to approach their problems in a variety of different ways. In addition, we know that the manner of working with the problem changes, depending upon in which phase of the process the patient is.» (p. 28) Later in the book, it becomes clear that the author sees psychodynamic understanding as being critical for healing, though only in the right phase. She writes: «We have to assume that the cause of not connecting properly with the patient depends upon our lack of understanding of what she is trying to show or tell us (...) The meaning of our work is not to try to get them to think right, but rather that we try together to understand why they think as they do. (...) It is a question of confirming the kernel of truth in what they are trying to get us to understand.»

The situation is complicated sometimes by the fact that the patient herself does not know what she wants to express, and is just trying things out. However, it is our task to search for a message until everything becomes more understandable for the patient.

On the subject of the development of psychosis, Levander writes: «Even if relapses occur, or if recovery seems to be delayed, some kind of development is taking place (...) The fact that feelings come more to the forefront is positive for the prognosis (...) elements of the emotional problems that forced them into psychosis can be found and processed.»

One question that everyone who works or is close to psychotic or psychotically inclined people is whether one can expect a complete improvement. Levander writes that some people become totally free while others have periods of turbulence during which the psychosis can reappear. Between these periods, some of these people appear to have totally recovered. Many people are never free from the threat of a relapse, while others experience their relapses as an important outlet for experiences that day to day life cannot offer. Most people are very fragile directly after a period of psychosis. Many of these are thrown back out into reality too quickly and relapse. Levander's view is that one should see these relapses as signs that daily life is more demanding than the patient can cope with and that the patient is in need of support, sometimes medication and always psychological understanding and help.

Periods of stagnation is a state I am familiar with, and these phases tend to make families and therapists despair. Levander describes how psychotic people sometimes have phases when they retreat from the demands and stimuli of the outside world. This is frustrating for others concerned, but can be interpreted in the way John Strauss does in «woodshedding».

This is like sitting down in a forest hut and waiting to catch up with oneself. Levander thinks that there is every reason to test the power of patience in periods like this.

On the subject of depression, Levander writes that «most patients have periods of depression. A part of their youth has gone missing; they have perhaps made a fool of themselves in the eyes of the world. (...) The patient must be allowed to mourn for what has been lost.»

The importance of having a crisis-perspective is highlighted in Levander's text, «Often, something that can never be regained has been lost, as in the case of accidents, deaths (...) In this context one can speak about the symptoms of psychosis as a reaction to a crisis – a desperate attempt at trying to hold onto the feeling of being someone» (p. 37).

«Above all, it is the so-called positive psychotic symptoms that are noticed by people: (...) hearing things that others can't hear (...) bizarre thoughts about the causes of the present situation (...) abrupt, incomprehensible emotional-shifts between despair, anger, icy superiority and confusion. (...) The feeling of being threatened by a catastrophe awakens anxiety, naturally. Some people find their need to sleep is diminishing (...) one is uncertain about what one dares to eat (...) The powerful inner tension is difficult to control, especially if one is feeling criticised and hurt.» (p. 49).

«The world is interpreted in a new way and one stands at the centre of events or of someone's attention. In order to escape the feeling of fragmentation, the person holds tightly onto these thoughts. The attempts of those around them to stop them from thinking like this are fruitless because the alternative is (...) psychological collapse». The experience is that «one has seen right through the meaning of things and that one understands things that most people have no knowledge about.» (p. 51).

«The longer these psychotic thoughts are allowed to live their own life without being challenged by a dialogue with other people, the greater is the risk that this inner world takes a firm grip.»

Aphasia and the extreme cognitive difficulties that my son, Tobias, has, and that deteriorate during a psychosis, make it impossible for him to explain the meaning of the symptoms himself. In some of the coming chapters, I describe how I try to find a meaning in Tobias' delusions during psychotic episodes. The fact that his brain injury has resulted in cognitive problems on a par with mental retardation has not made things any easier.

Let us return to Levander, who thinks that in the case of developmental disabilities «the staff's task will be to not only encourage but even to help find the words to express what the patient can't express herself. The more difficulties the patient has in communicating (...) the greater must be the staff's efforts to give her a feeling of being there (...) The patient must have the feeling of being someone with experiences worthy of attention, despite the conviction of being totally worthless. In this way, the weak self-esteem can be slowly strengthened.»

It is here that Levander reaches the core of the struggle about what treatment should be focused upon. Should we focus treatment upon the brain's organic, chemical imbalance, and that the role of the staff is to provide support while the medication does the major work, or should relationships, community, understanding, meaning and context be the major elements of the treatment, while medication is used as a supportive element when necessary?

Does one need to be a psychotherapist to have any practical use of the examples in this book? No, even staff lacking higher qualifications in psychotherapy and psychology can do a great deal. When I read Sonja Levander's advice to the staff at treatment centres, I recognized my own eagerness to try to convince the personal assistants, and staff in day centres, of their immense importance in achieving a well-balanced approach. She writes: «In the day room, it is a question

41

of «just being», which is a very important ability for those working with psychotic patients.» And «some people have a special aptitude for this kind of interaction. They can switch between everyday chat about things like how to fix a plug, and helping to divert a patient out of a discussion that is threatening to get out of hand.» (Levander, 2007, p. 61).

Benedetti describes how during psychosis one loses one's *ego boundaries*. Integrity gets erased and displaced. He gives examples of patients asking whether they are one or two people.

Schizophrenic people also have difficulties in distinguishing between themselves and others, which threatens their freedom to make decisions for themselves. Sensory impressions are often confusing and difficult to interpret. This also applies to how they experience their own body. Benedetti writes that in schizophrenia it is especially apparent that the patient becomes very egocentric in the sense that everything that takes place is construed to be about the person herself, that it is either aimed at her, or caused by her (Benedetti, 1990).

A similar self-centeredness often underlies social phobia or excessive shyness. A lack of self-esteem leads to a distressing preoccupation with how one is seen by other people, as well as a fear of being exposed as being incompetent.

In my supervision of staff working with persons with brain damage, a lot of time goes to understanding *negative countertransference* as it is called in psychodynamic psychology. Benedetti perfectly describes the staff's unease: «The greatest source of unease for the therapist is the hopelessness of the situation that one is involved in». Later in the text, the connection to negative counter-transference is made: «negative counter-transference can be a source of therapeutic unease! Impatience, incomprehension, a latent aversion to the patient, and many of his qualities, uncertainty and confusion come in conflict with the therapeutic necessity of being on the side of the patient. (...) the negative emotions arise from the patient's aggression, the pain that he causes to others and his ever present neurotic pride.» (...) «Being aware of negative counter-transference feelings shouldn't be seen as a problem. Quite often, we see that the patient has in fact developed. It would seem as if they feel that we understand them when we put up with the more difficult sides of their characters. Our negative counter-transference is their aggression that we carry in order to mix it with libido[4]. A large part of the patient's destructivity diminishes since it has not been the cause of ruining our relationship ...» (Benedetti, 1990).

The risk that unconscious transference complicates the working atmosphere if they are not brought to the surface, as in a psychodynamic supervision, is also described by Thomas Johansson. He believes that institutions and organizations that have the task of taking care of society's disabled individuals «tend to be flooded with primitive anxiety and to develop destructive defence mechanisms (...) In this case, the Kleinian school of thought with its well-developed theory about defence structures, early anxiety, containing functions, jealousy and the importance of verbalising matters that threaten to ruin a group or organisation can play an important role.» (Johansson, 2000).

To understand communication «Mother was the Earth»

In his book about psychotherapy with psychotic people, Jackson describes how he had help in developing his diagnostic and therapeutic interview method from Melanie Klein's further development of the work of Freud. It had «a major influence upon my attempts to understand a large amount of confusing material ...» By trying to grasp what the patient was trying to say through her symbolic communications,

4 A psychoanalytic concept meaning the life-giving energy of love and sexuality

43

and the personal questions underlying seemingly mundane comments, Jackson noticed that he could create contact with his psychotic patients.

Jackson quotes a patient: «I have never thought about it before, that I was jealous about Keith, or that mother was the Earth, but she was. That was how I felt in relation to her.»

I recognise this. Tobias becomes extremely engrossed in the Earth, the cosmos, the universe, and his closeness to me, his mother. There are a number of examples of this in the coming chapters.

As regards defence-mechanisms: Jackson relates a dialogue with a patient who is slightly psychotic. She tells him that she has dropped her fixation with outer space, but that she wants to be loved. However, she is occupied by the fear that the radio doesn't work, that the staff is experimenting with her head, that the telephone is strange, etc. Jackson concentrates on her need to feel loved and interprets everything she says in terms of lost love until the patient successively dares to drop the symbolical circumlocutions and starts talking about real relationships. «It is perfectly possible to understand her, given one knows primitive mechanisms such as splitting, projection, introjections, concrete thinking, and confusion about the present and the past.» (Jackson & Williams, 1997).

The risk of a chronic state

In the above, I have presented a number of approaches aimed at preventing relapses and avoiding a chronic state of psychosis. A standard medical approach is that patients should have a maintenance dose to prevent a relapse. The more psychologically-oriented therapist, such as myself, maintains that psychological support is of the utmost importance for the patient's recovery from the fragility that is inevitable after an acute psychosis. To what extent medication is necessary in this phase varies from person to person. Jackson and his co-authors have a more outright psychological approach.

«Much of contemporary psychiatry aims at removing or suppressing symptoms by anti-psychotic medication so that the patient can be discharged and return to society (...) This will be the start of a vicious circle with relapses and finally a chronic state. This means that one has failed (not even tried) to explain the reason for the attack, and its importance within the patient's relations and life story.»

The author considers that one has to try to understand how and why the crisis has arisen, and if one does not manage to understand the meaning of the patient's psychosis as a reaction to a crisis and a breakdown, «a secondary disability is created – a very iatrogenic injury – arising from the consolidation of the psychosis mechanisms.» An iatrogenic injury is one that has arisen as a result of incorrect treatment. The author refers to other authors who have described the same things: «Pau (1979) (...) also describes a group that developed from a less difficult state to a chronically worsened state of schizophrenia as a result of insufficient treatment or institutionalisation.» The author also refers to Pylkkanen, 1989, and Cullberg, 1991, who have both stated that a large number of chronically psychotic patients have an illness that is in reality iatrogenic (Jackson & Williams, 1997).

An important question to ask is whether health care is guilty of causing iatrogenic injuries when patients with a brain injury are medicated for depression, anxiety and epilepsy without, or instead of, a psychotherapeutic trauma treatment. The difference between health and disease is discussed by the psychologist, Sigvard Lingh, in «Läkartidningen». He mentions an interesting view made by an organisation that caters for the rights of people with epilepsy. They suggest that epilepsy should be viewed as a state and not an illness. The text in its original state can be viewed at: http://www.epilepsy. org.uk/press/facts.html, 2006-02-01 (Lingh, 2006). The view expressed by this organization as referred to by Lingh corresponds very well with my own opinion that epilepsy is an intensively alert state of mind. Without thinking, health care staff medicates an illness, while the state itself can perhaps be treated psychologically?

PTSD and intensive care

Memories from intensive care can result in anxiety and a lowered quality of life. One in four patients that needed intensive care after an accident had memories of nightmares, hallucinations and paranoid memories of experiencing that the staff were trying to hurt them (Ringdal, 2008). This would mean that the patients have a double trauma. Firstly, the one caused by an accident that they don't consciously remember, but that has left its mark in the body-memory, unconsciously. Secondly, the unconscious, unprocessed experiences of intensive care, with states of confusion, anaesthesia, and disorientation throughout.

These experiences combined: post-traumatic memories on two levels, an impaired brain function, communication difficulties, and the lost self-respect which is inevitable in the case of a loss of intellectual capacity, give every reason to believe that individuals who have had an accident with a resulting brain injury, have the psychological prerequisites for the development of a psychotic state. The brain's inability to maintain, interpret, and make anxiety comprehensible, multiplied with the loss of functions, loss of identity, loss of friends, and the loss of abilities and future opportunities, multiplied by flashbacks[5] of a near-death experience ... It is easy to understand that normal, «healthy» defence-mechanisms such as repression are inadequate. Despite being painful, especially for close relatives, it is very understandable that fragmentation, projection and escapism will be the solutions.

---

5 A flashback is a psychological phenomenon in which the person experiences something from her past, often in the form of rapid snapshots. It can arise after traumatic events, e.g. from childhood. Source: http://sv.wikipedia.org/wiki/Flashback_(psykologi)

In the following chapters, I will write about this and other small daily cares, nuisances and pleasures. I end my theoretical discussion and references at this point. From here, I invite the reader to follow me on a breathtaking journey that I never asked for, but that has left me speechless with admiration. What do I admire? Tobias, the power of love, and the incomprehensible wisdom of psychoanalysis, which is so easy to reject if one hasn't seen psychosis from the inside. Welcome then to Tobias' life during the ten years that have followed since the publication of «There is Someone in there».

REFERENCES

Benedetti, Gaetano (1990) *Den farliga kärleken – om psykoterapi vid psykoser*. Dualis förlag. ISBN 91-87852-03-9

Bicknell, D.J. Living with a mentally handicapped member of the family. *Postgrad Med Journal 1982* 58: 597-605. Internet version: http://pmj.bmj.com/cgi/reprintform

Bohuslänningen, lördag 12 januari 2002. Del 2. s. 15

Brain, C. quoted in: Wallin, K. Bilden av psykiatrin. Ett seminarium på Jonsereds Herrgård 9 november 2007. *www. jonseredsherrgard.se*

Carlberg, I. (2008) *Pillret. En berättelse om depressioner och doktorer, forskare och Freud, människor och marknader*. Stockholm: Norstedts.

DSM-IV-TR® Diagnostic and Statistical Manual of Mental Disorders. Fourth Edition, Text Revision. American Psychiatric Publishing, Inc.

Enqvist, B. (1997) Presurgical Hypnosis and Suggestions in Anesthesia. *Hypnos vol XXIV no 4-1997 s. 193-195.* Welins Tryckeri Örebro. ISSN 0282-5090

Enqvist, B. (2004) *Inbjudan till trance. Hypnos i vård och terapi.* Uppsala: Mareld. www.mareld.se

Enqvist, B. & Bengtsson, K. (2005) *Orden som läker. Kommunikation och möten i vård och terapi.* Lund: Studentlitteratur.

Hagberg-van›t Hooft, I. (2005) Inst. f kvinnors och barns hälsa, K.I. http://diss.kib.se/2005/91-7140-380-9.

Jackson, Murray & Williams, Paul (1997) *Ofattbara stormar. Att söka förstå psykosen.* Sthlm: Natur & Kultur. ISBN 91-27-05597-3

Johansson, Thomas (2000) *Psykosens inre landskap.* Lund: Studentlitteratur. ISBN 91-44-01554-2

Johnson, K. & Korn, E. (1986) Hypnosis and Imagery in the Rehabilitation of a Brain-Damaged Patient. *Hypnos XIII, 3-1986.* ISSN 0282-5090

Klein, M. (1988/1993) *Kärlek, Skuld och Gottgörelse.* Sthlm: Natur och Kultur. ISBN 91-27-03789-4

Komitova, M., Johansson B. & Eriksson, P. (2006) On neural plasticity, new neurons and the post ischemic milieu: An integrated view on experimental rehabilitation. *Experimental Neurology, 2006, vol.199, no 1, s. 42-55.* Elsevier Science B.V.

Levander, S. (2007) *Om psykoser och psykosbehandling.* Sthlm: Mareld Böcker. ISBN 9789188872838.

Lingh, S. (2006) Det finns mer än en definition av begreppet hälsa. *Läkartidningen nr 17, 2006 volym 103.*

Meares, A. (1986/1999) *Avspänd utan mediciner.* Sthlm: Natur & Kultur.

Ringdal, Mona (2008) Memories and Health Related Quality of Life – in patients with trauma cared for in the Intensive Care Unit. (Academic paper) Institute of Health and Care Sciences. Sahlgrenska Academy, Göteborgs Universitet. http://hdl.handle.net/2077/18650

Rossi, Ernest L. (2005) The Memory Trace Reactivation and Reconstruction Theory of Therapeutic Hypnosis: The Creative Replaying of Gene Expression and Brain Plasticity in Stroke Rehabilitation. *Hypnos, vol XXXII, no 1-2005, s. 5-16.* Welins Tryckeri Örebro. ISSN 0282-5090

Schlaug, G. The Neurosciences and Music III Disorders and Plasticity. *Annals of the New York Academy of Sciences, vol 1169, 2009. s. 372*

Spellacy, F. (1992) Hypnotherapy following Traumatic Brain Injuries. *Hypnos. Vol XIX no 1-1992.* Welins Tryckeri Örebro. ISSN 0282-5090

THERE IS SOMEONE IN THERE. A SUMMARY

My previous book is about a healthy 23 year-old man that suffers a life-long disability. It is about all parents' greatest fear: that their child will be involved in an accident, losing intelligence, mobility, speech and other functions that we associate with a full life.

A bicycle accident took away my son's life as it was at that point. I describe just how multifaceted this process can be: it contains despair, sadness, hope, strength from above, love and meaning.

During the four years after the trauma, my position is that of a mother and a psychologist. My knowledge of psychology is so

Drawing Tobias made 10 years after the accident

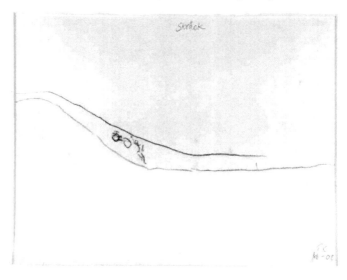

internalized by now that I can never ignore the psychological perspective. Sometimes, in health-care situations, I was treated as if it had been better if I had left my professional knowledge behind at work and behaved like an ignorant mother.

On the evening of the 2nd of August 1996, I was awakened from a deep sleep by the sound of the telephone. My husband, Tore, answered and I heard his voice say «fallen off his bike?»

Our oldest son, Tobias, had fallen off his bike and we were to go to the Emergency Room. One thing we realized directly is that one doesn't phone to a 23 year-old man's parents, and ask them to come directly, if the situation isn't critical.

Finally arrived at the Emergency Intake at the hospital, we were received by a nice nurse who informed us that «Tobias has a skull injury, perhaps more. He is in X-ray right now, and will go directly to the operating theatre. As soon as the operation is finished we will inform you.»

We reacted so differently! Tobias' girlfriend's father watched ice hockey in the staff's room, as did Tobias' friend when he wasn't writing about it or sleeping on the sofa. His girlfriend went out to smoke, as did Tore. Most of us walked restlessly or dispelled our thoughts in different ways, which is understandable, when you think about how helpless we were.

Mårten, Tobias' two-year younger brother, came up to me. He hugged me hard and just cried, cried and cried. «It's not true» he said «it's a movie». He had a white, bloodied towel wrapped round his right hand. He wasn't hurt, it was Tobias' blood.

Eventually, the operation was over and we were given some information. In the book, I describe how I, mother in crisis, was so over-sensitive about tone of voice and the manner in which we were informed. For example, the anaesthetist who was responsible for the anaesthesia during the operation told us about it clearly, and simply, without any sympathy in her voice. She did everything correctly, but I was still so mad at her, although I understood that I must not show her how I felt.

Just a few days later I found that she was wonderful with her direct honesty, her natural thoughtfulness, and humility in the face of our helpless existence. But right then I could only love someone who could promise me that Tobias would be alive and well. I understood that no one could do that.

At six o'clock on Saturday, Tore and I went home to try to get some sleep. We sat at the boat terminal and awaited our boat. Off the boat from the islands came a father with his son. The boy was seemingly disabled and retarded in some way. I cried and looked towards Tore. Was this our future? We hardly dared think about it.

It took time for us to get used to Tobias' disability. The book's four-year time scale is about the struggle to adapt to the change and the battle to get back as many of his lost abilities as possible.

The first months were a question of re-establishing basic functions such as being able to urinate and to get beyond the painful and infectious catheter draining. I looked at this from the perspective of trauma with the basic assumption that the inhibition was psychological. I made use of hypnosis techniques in order to disperse the inhibition and to calm Tobias so that the association between the trauma, and urinating, losing control, losing consciousness and almost dying, was resolved. Here is a small extract from that communication:

He is not conscious of the reasons for his fear, of course: partly because of the memory loss caused by his brain injury, and partly because a life-threatening mental trauma is usually relegated to the haze of the unconscious. I suggest a relaxation technique that involves me counting downwards. He agrees but remains tense and somewhat restless. I ask him if he is afraid of coming into contact with something frightening. Tobias nods. I promise not to push him and to make sure that he will be fine no matter what happens. Tobias puts his thumb up – his latest sign for okay - and seems to trust me. I continue the relaxation instructions and make use of the countdown technique, and then tell him about a detective that is inside Tobias' head, searching for the causes of tensions, and I ask this detective to show Tobias what he finds. Tobias moves a little restlessly and I ask him if he needs to urinate. He confirms this so I go and fetch the urine bottle. Tobias tries but nothing happens. After a short while he tires of trying and indicates that he doesn't need to, which is certainly not true. I say that there is obviously something hindering Tobias from peeing and I try a so-called theatre visualization technique. This is the name of the method even though one can just as easily imagine a TV or a cinema screen instead of a stage. The aim of the technique is to help the unconscious to project its images upon an imaginary stage or screen so that it becomes visible for the inner eye. Tobias is to imagine a cinema and he will press my hand when he is there. «Yes», he's there. He can decide himself whether he is there alone or with other people. He wants to be there alone. He can decide the type of cinema curtain and its colour. He suddenly looks up, lifts his head, searches with his eyes, sees me, looks calm, lowers his head and closes his eyes again.

I continue: «When the curtain goes up you will see what you need to know, what you need to see on the screen in order that you will continue to heal as well as possible. The curtain is being raised now, look carefully ...»

Tobias opens his eyes, looks straight ahead, looks extremely surprised, looks at me and tries to say something that sounds like «a…e». He repeats «a, e».

«Did you see something?»

«Yes»

«Yourself?»

«Yes»

«a e, does that mean: am dead?»

«Yes!»

«So that is what it was that you needed to know, that you thought you were going to die, perhaps you were, in fact, dead for a short while.»

Tobias seems to be very interested.

«Then you perhaps want to hear what happened later?» I ask and get a yes. I tell him how Mårten came after him on his bike and found Tobias lying seemingly lifeless on the pavement, not breathing, not seeing, with blood flowing out of the crushed side of his head. I tell him how Mårten put his hand over the wound to try and stop the flow of blood and then he whispered in his ear: «You must breathe, Tobias, you must breathe!» I tell him how Mårten breathed in his ear at a rate that he thought suitable, and about how Tobias started to breathe.

When I tell him this, Tobias starts to cry, and hugs me. He cries for a long time while I hold him tightly. He is relieved in every way, because he urinates now, as well. A whole litre, in fact.

Rehabilitation, the phase that follows acute hospital care, is dealt with in the second half of the book. Healthcare's medical approach to treatment collided with my psychological approach towards the rights of the patients and more importantly, the importance of feelings for the healing of a trauma and for the possibilities of development.

Here is an extract from my description of an information meeting arranged by rehabilitation staff for a large group of newly-registered patients and their families:

«Here, it is the patients who are centre of focus» and «Relatives are very important», are oft-repeated phrases. We are told about their views on the various behavioural changes that might arise following a brain injury. Depression is especially mentioned as a common problem after skull or brain injuries, «but we have medicines for this» says a psychologist who smiles towards a doctor, who in turn praises the psychologist's capability as regards investigating and diagnosing patients' brain damage, and also supporting patients and staff in planning treatment. (...) We, who want to take responsibility for our own lives, are problematic, as we question ingrained professional routines, we question authority and we question decisions. And all the time we wonder if there is any point in it, we wonder whether we will make a difference at all, whether a candid exchange of thoughts is possible. Maybe we are just causing insecurity and defensiveness?

At one point, Tore accompanies Tobias to the physiotherapist. He takes the opportunity to tell her about how we have managed to get Tobias to bend his right knee. She does not appreciate this collegial attitude, and kindly tells Tore that she is the physiotherapist and he is the parent, and that the parent's job is to take the patient out in his wheelchair – «go to the pizzeria or something like that».

I was once rebuked by a doctor, after she had read in Tobias' contact book about our plans for the weekend. We were planning to congratulate grandmother on her birthday, Tobias was to sleep one night at his girlfriend's place, and the rest of the time we would be in our house. The doctor called me to her office and told me that we couldn't let Tobias be in three different places during the weekend. The devil flew into me and I decided to test her humanity by asking her how she would have done if she were in my place. She fell into the trap and answered! In other words, she took it upon herself to choose between grandmother and girlfriend. The assistant doctor who was also there made the opposite choice, falling thus into the same trap of choosing for us. I'm not proud of myself for using this strategy – to tempt them out and to show their authoritarian colours. However, it is in fact so doctors are expected to behave. Many patients and relatives believe that doctors know best, even in matters in which they have less knowledge than the patients and their family. I am not only critical in the book; I also give many examples of ways in which a respectful interaction can be achieved, as in the following case:

I wish that the staff could distinguish between problem and solution: I wish they would tell us what the problem is rather than suggest their own solution to a problem that they have not even defined. In this case, in the above example, the doctor, who has identified a problem, could have contacted us and said something like «By the way, I am worried that Tobias won't get the rest he needs if he is going to be in a number of places during the weekend, what's your opinion?» Another way of expressing the problem as the doctor sees it could be like this: «I see from Tobias' contact book that he is going to be at three different places this weekend. This made me worried because, in our experience, many close relatives fail to see the need for rest at the weekend after a week of tough training here. Have you thought about how to make sure he gets his rest during a weekend like this one?»

One chapter deals with soul-searching. Parents, who have children that expose themselves to risks such as cycling under the influence of alcohol and without a helmet, driving motorbikes too fast or living recklessly, often reflect upon their own guilt. It is obvious to me, as a psychologist with a psychodynamic, existential orientation, that one must respect these kinds of considerations. Guilt shouldn't just be diverted, comforted away or denied. Guilt can be healthy and release energy as long as it doesn't paralyse self-esteem and a feeling of worthiness despite everything, despite shortcomings and faults. It is difficult.

I give a wealth of examples of communication and hypnosis that are useful when treating brain-injured people, psychologically. One example is the possibility of inducing calm when an epileptic fit starts, as well as stopping, easing or delaying it. The model I use is based upon hypnosis in the sense that I offer an idea that is metaphorically similar to the processes in the brain during a seizure. The metaphor corresponds to the electrical surge with a subsequent discharge that is characteristic for epilepsy as I understand it. Tobias was to imagine his scars as being an enormous gap. I used the American word «canyon» because sometimes it is easier for Tobias to understand English words and also because a canyon is a very big and deep gap. I couldn't find a better word in Swedish for what I wanted Tobias to visualise. I then described how electricity guys came and expected that the old roads would still pass through right there, but no! So they gather at the brink and crowd and push. In order to avoid an attack, a current jump over the gap, Tobias was to instruct the guys to build new ways, to go round the canyon, and most important of all, to take it easy. If at any time Tobias found it impossible to stop the seizure, then I instructed him to firmly ask the guys to not jump all at the same time, to take it «one by one!»

I have always been led to believe that epilepsy is a form of hyperactivity in the brain and that one can explain an epileptic seizure as a sort of electrical discharge. Despite the fact that one still measures brain activity with electroencephalogram, EEG, that in fact means «measure the electricity of the brain/meninges» and that one uses EEG to measure epileptic activity specifically, it still is seen as news that epilepsy is a question of electrically-transferred impulses in the membranes of the brain. A team of researchers under Cunningham in Newcastle found that epileptic activity within a group of patients consisted of electrically-, not chemically-transferred signals, which, if one believes the researchers, was what was believed earlier. Cunningham draws the conclusion that this is why 30% of all patients with epilepsy are unaffected by medication. The experiment involved asking permission of patients whose brain was to be operated to be allowed to measure the activity of the removed brain tissue. They found an electrical wavelength, a pulsation, an oscillation, which was assumed to precede an epileptic seizure. Since anti- epileptic medicines have an effect at a chemical level, it was thus presumed that this is why medication has no effect on electrically-induced epilepsy (Cunningham, 2009).

I am surprised at the obvious lack of a holistic approach to this sort of research. The simple fact that the brain is involved in chemical processes does not exclude the fact that it may work via electrical impulses as well! Unfortunately, I can't remember the source, but in a textbook on the brain it states that the electricity model is obsolete and that modern neurology considers brain functions to be chemically-based. This can't be true though. The fact that EEG is still used ought to mean that electricity is still thought to be involved.

At some point during medical research's development, the idea that the brain's internal communication was based on electricity was abandoned in favour of biochemical processes. I suspect that the pharmaceutical industry has influenced developments in a, for it, profitable direction. Through research in chemistry, these financiers can get a return on their investments. Pharmaceuticals are based on chemistry. In some strange way, the medical community was persuaded to lose interest in the electrical impulses of the brain. Thus, when Cunningham and his team found that epilepsy, at least the form that is resistant to medication, is triggered by electrical oscillations, this is seen as news, as something unexpected.

Yet, when the first edition of this book was proof-read by neurological experts, nobody questioned my common sense hypothesis that Tobias' epilepsy could be likened to a flash of lightning and an electrical discharge. I have always understood epilepsy to be some kind of electrical current, and used the metaphor that small guys (electrons) crowd around waiting to jump over the gap (scar-tissue) that, before the brain-injury, was a wide path (nerve-cell or synapse) but has since been broken or blocked. The small guys collect there till they jump. And if they jump at the same time, parts of the body cramp and shake. The discharge is abnormal in the sense of being extreme and violent, since the circuitry is damaged or overactive. Everyone who has read the book has found the image reasonable, and that includes neurologists.

I also describe how the psychological treatment of patients with left-hemisphere brain damage should combine the traditional psychodynamic respect for the healing power of insight with the psycho-educational approach of creating structure when cognitive functions are missing. An example of structure can be tempus, since patients with aphasia may have difficulty in distinguishing between words denoting the past and the present. We psychologists cannot assume that when we are talking in the past-tense form, the aphasic patients understand that this has already taken place. Thus, I hope that those who have not already read the book now will want to read *There is Someone in there*, both for inspiration and psychological knowledge.

In order to get the most out of the present book, the reader will need to know more about Tobias' brain injury.

Tobias injuries are localized to the front and middle part of the left anterior half of the brain, roughly from the ear and around it all the way up to the top of the skull. The left hemisphere of the brain houses, in its frontal parts, functions that are essential for expressive speech, its central parts are important for movement and the ability to feel the opposite half of the body, while in its rear part, are areas that are important for the understanding of language. Tobias had difficulties with all of these functions i.e. difficulties in understanding and producing a spoken language (aphasia), and a right-sided paralysis (palsy), along with sensory disturbances. The orbit frontal cortex, which among other things is concerned with inhibition control, seemed quite undamaged, but when Tobias is frail and tired he can still be primitively exempted from many of the inhibitions that belong to a civilized behaviour. Tobias understands what he hears, but not the exact meaning of the words. This is true of both nouns in particular and verbs in general. Adjectives that describe feelings and relationships are intact and one can probably assume that this sort of language involves the right side of the brain, which was unscathed. Tobias cannot express himself numerically other than a word here and there. He also has severe memory disorders, especially memories that are dependent upon verbal language. Although his eyes and ears work, his ability to interpret what he registers in his right visual field and his right ear is impaired. As far as his sight is concerned, Tobias has total vision loss for the right vision field, in other words, 50% blindness. After a time he learned to compensate for this by twisting his head and catching whatever was to be seen to the right. However, he often relapses into neglect, which means that he acts as if his vision covers the entire field, resulting in collisions with everything that is to the right of his own «nose line».

As regards his hearing, one can say that what goes into his right ear passes over to the left side of the brain and isn't understood. However, we realised after a time that if one called his attention, he could concentrate and listen as well as understand what was said even if one was standing on his right side. If, however, one didn't catch his attention first then the speech was only perceived as background noise, and didn't catch his attention. Tobias ability to think in abstract terms was also damaged. Because of this, Tobias lost his ability to understand letters as sound symbols and thus his ability to read. The right half of the brain's ability to think in images compensates somewhat for this deficit, enabling him to learn to recognise the commonest words in headlines and on signs. He also taught himself to sound out the letters of words from left to right so that he could read individual words. This, however, was a slow process.

The left hemisphere of the brain is involved in being able to plan, so there were problems with this as well. The logistics of making a cup of tea took Tobias about six years to learn, and when he had learnt it, it was always with the same routine, and only in his own kitchen. He couldn't teach himself to transfer knowledge to other subjects or other tools. He could put on his clothes using his left hand, but couldn't learn to adapt his clothing to the weather. However, in later years he did learn to ask for advice. In this case, insight played a large part in this development. I feel that I have given sufficient background information. I have not really wanted to give a comprehensive picture of Tobias' disabilities and resources. In fact, there have been constant discoveries, every day, every month, every year. It is only possible to describe the occasional event, as I have in *There is Someone in there* and in the coming chapters. Every person is unique and full of surprises. This will be confirmed if one is interested enough.

REFERENCE

Cunningham, M. & Whittington, M. (2009) Research sheds new light on epilepsy. *Newcastle Biomedicine*. 30 November. Newcastle University, Newcastle upon Tyne.

*Tobias in a bewildering
situation of loss*

TO REALIZE OR TO AVOID REALIZING. THE IMPORTANCE OF INSIGHT

The personal assistant, G, texts to my husband that Tobias seems to be disoriented and he wonders whether they should cancel the body-therapy. For the sake of simplicity, I will call it body-therapy but as the current method is not an approved health and care treatment in Sweden, the legally correct term is pedagogy. The method in question is the Feldenkrais method.

So, Tobias seems disoriented today. He does have a brain injury and this is why he is disoriented sometimes, it is a part of the picture. Besides, Tobias had an epileptic seizure the night before last, which gives even further cause for tiredness and absent-mindedness. The Feldenkrais pedagogue has said that it is pointless to attend on days when Tobias is incapable of focusing and concentrating. It is better to make a cancellation.

If we accept that advice, Tobias should cancel today's treatment.

I shall now view it from a psychological position. I speak to Tobias over the phone during the morning. The conversation goes something like this: «How are you today?» «Fine.» I ask a few more questions to see how things are and in order to check on how communicable Tobias is. He seems sufficiently clear-headed to be able to talk with me, at least as far as his aphasia allows.

«It seems you have an appointment with Thomas Bergagård, Feldenkrais today.»

«Yes, but no!»

«You're not going to go?»

«No.»

I can hear by his tone of voice that it *could be* an avoiding-no. A «no» that means: I don't want to take part in life just now; I want to keep myself to myself.

  I attempt at this point an exploratory talk that maybe increases awareness:

«Saying no to Feldenkrais can depend on several things. It is perhaps because you are feeling a bit uncertain about it as it has been a while since your last visit. Because when you've been there several times in row and a routine has been built up and you feel you have mastered the method, you enjoy the progress you make and really want to go there. However, it is only you who can judge whether you would manage to be focused today in the way that is necessary with Thomas.»

«Hmm, yes.»

«So the question is; what is making you distracted? It is usually because your self-esteem is lowered for some reason.»

Silence.

«How are you feeling about yourself just now? Do you like yourself?»

«Nah, so so ...»

«You have had a new assistant during the earlier part of the week, Lis. Do you remember?»

«Yes.»

«Your self-confidence usually gets a knock when you have a young woman as an assistant. Before your accident, women of your own age were your best friends, and when you wanted to you could charm them so that they fell in love with you. And you knew it. And you liked this charming person that you were. Lis is a woman who will help you with your daily life, now, assist you because of your difficulties. This is not how you want it. It's difficult. So you want to turn off the world.»

«Yes, you're right.»

«Yes, this is how your life is ... now. But, you're getting better and better (his favourite expression). I think you must consider whether you want to concentrate on body-therapy today, about whether you have the energy to concentrate and go to the Feldenkrais ... or if you feel you can't manage, that life is difficult, and that you would rather come to us on Brännö. We can talk and give you strength till you feel better again.»

«Hmm ...» (Silence).

«Or perhaps just stay at home and do nothing ... although that's perhaps not such a good idea?»

«No.»

«In that case, G (the assistant) knows what you're struggling with, when you seem introvert and confused. You can think about when you want to come to us. You are always welcome.»

«Yes, good.»

I talk to G who tells me that Anneli, the assistant who has worked longest with Tobias, has expressed the same theory as I have.

Thoughts

A discussion like this one can be of great importance for avoiding further confusion. In Tobias' case, confusion that has not been understood and is neglected or met with an awkward silence can lead to psychosis with paranoid tendencies and irrational ideas about being specially chosen to create an alternative way of living on another planet.

It doesn't help just to be positive in this situation, to just list his strengths and resources. It is worth mentioning this since the trend these days, if you go as far as consulting a psychologist, is to work future-oriented, reinforcing and supportive. It is true that in the situation described above, it is important to reinforce Tobias, which is what I do, but it is just as important to affirm Tobias' situation just as it is, namely the loss of his seductive, adult, male power. He is no longer the charmer that he once was, not in that way. He had the power of speech and he could give verbal notice of his lively intelligence. In other words, he had all that was needed to charm most attractive and intelligent women.

Can one cope with this kind of insight? No, not all at once! Yes, a bit at a time. And it is difficult. But what is the alternative? The alternative is to avoid facing up to losses, but I have learned in my profession that the price for such avoidance is stagnation. Every denial of loss is to shun an inner reality. Avoidance becomes a habitual strategy with the aim of denying everything that reminds one of the losses. This defence mechanism must be activated when one watches TV, walks around town and sees strong, healthy people walking in twos, when old friends get married and have children, when a sibling starts a new generation in the form of a new family … yes, there is a constant swarm of events surrounding Tobias that he has to deny if he is to avoid this pain.

In my work, I see many victims, families and even staff who choose avoidance as their primary strategy. For this very reason, the victims probably seem to be less bright than they in fact are. They are less creative, less curious, more inflexible, more depressed, shielded, irritable, moody and unpredictable. If one isn't better informed, one can come to believe that the symptoms of avoidance are purely physical and a kind of neurological expression of the injured brain's random signals and connections.

I draw conclusions from the example above, of course. Since this is the first chapter with illustrations from life, I will give an account of my conclusions at this point so that my ideology and my views about treatment based on experience are made clear. These factors will naturally influence the choice of material that I will make use of in the rest of the book.

Rehab or assistance organisations, as well as families who are considering consulting a psychologist or psychotherapist, should hire someone who has wide and deep knowledge. In other words, they should hire someone who is acquainted with brain injuries and their repercussions as well as having knowledge about contemporary psychodynamic, existential theories and is experienced in insight-oriented and supportive counselling techniques.

The existential viewpoint has been clarified by the researcher, Pamela Klonoff. In her book from 2010, she gives a thorough description of the practice of psychotherapy with patients with a brain injury. She recommends counselling and psycho-educative methods. Psycho-educative can be defined as «pedagogical methods with the psyche in focus». The goals of the treatment are awareness, acceptance, and realism. It pleases me that someone has dared to point out that this is possible and that Klonoff maintains that awareness helps one to grieve, which in turn makes way for acceptance and realism. Realism is made possible if the therapist helps the patient to talk about her loss of self-esteem, identity and place in society.

And a new meaning in life, quality of life, self-realization and hope can be sought as awareness grows. One of the prominent figures in existentialism, Yalom, is repeatedly quoted. Everybody's longing for and right to meaning and self-realization is focused upon in this practical book (Klonoff, 2010).

However, I would have liked to see sections on psychological methods for the treatment of anxiety and depression, psychotic symptoms and signs of PTSD. The case studies give the impression that the author fully trusts the medication of such symptoms. What is more, the case studies and tips show that the group of patients the book is based upon is not among the more severely injured. The patients are expected to be able to write a certain amount, to read, speak, to make use of strategies to help memory etceteraetcetera.

So, I hope for more clinical documentation of patients that lack language, who hide from sadness behind depressive symptoms, who have high levels of anxiety, who dissociate, who have flashbacks and who cannot control their anger and their escape from reality. Psychodynamic theory and hypnosis-influenced methods can be of use in these cases.

As will be seen in the coming chapters, insight-oriented psychotherapy is possible with patients with severe brain injuries, as long as one can give hope, confidence, and a feeling that it is meaningful. Those people who warn about insight presume that insight automatically results in insecurity and higher anxiety-levels. In a report about ADHD in a book by Lingh (2010), Doctor Hirvikoski and others write that «raised insight through psychotherapy or psycho-education can have negative effects». I described similar concerns in my earlier book when I described how the neuropsychologist warned me about using hypnosis as it could lead to anxiety. This is true, of course. They are right, given that the psychotherapist is incompetent or inexperienced in dealing with anxiety in patients with cognitive dysfunction.

Psychodynamic competence involves searching for the function of symptoms, and the logic behind this is that if you really dare to see, you often find a deeper meaning beneath the most absurd behaviour. If you seriously come to understand this, then the question «How to do?» will be irrelevant. You will explore.

When you haven't the strength to understand, or when you are perhaps unaware that understanding is possible, you will be helpless when faced with incomprehensible and bizarre behaviour. Care staff, as well as families, often lack a theory to enable them to manage these feelings of helplessness and insufficiency. In this situation, you are very liable to contact a pedagogic counsellor or «coach» who can help with methods and tips and who says: Do this and do that!

I do this myself, sometimes, in my role as a supervisor. However, the best situation is when I supervise groups over a longer period of time so that they can learn the basics of an existential dynamic approach.

Does practical advice help? Perhaps. It might help staff to cope with their feelings of helplessness for a while, and to make use of methods that an expert has taught them. In this way they avoid having the heavy responsibility of finding ways and means with the help of their own judgement and intuition, which is a most difficult thing to do. However, as a supervisor, I want to give them more than this. I want to create conditions that foster understanding, empathy and reflection. My psychodynamic existential orientation reminds me to dare appreciate the difficult path of trying, together with the staff, to understand their role in depth, which also means supporting them in their personal development. This is done by an examination of their emotions, and an awareness of their reactions, needs and desires. When this is achieved, and the level of consciousness of the staff is higher, they will have the motivation to try to understand what deeper motives and needs lie behind the reactions of the patient/client.

This kind of approach requires a level of maturity on behalf of the supervisor, who has to support the staff, whose unanswered questions may cause them frustration and worry. The supervisor must both put up with and be a role-model herself in showing that a listening approach and an open attitude are stronger tools for the work process in the long run than just trying to find the right techniques. There are both constructive and destructive approaches and the difference lies in having the courage to try to understand the meaning, intentions and needs of those one is working with.

There are two personality traits one must watch out for among staff working with people with disabilities. The first is a lack of self-knowledge. The other is a tendency to present oneself as being perfect. Should these two traits be combined, careful supervision and guidance is needed, although this may not help anyway. A lack of self-knowledge together with a need to be seen as perfect is a dangerous combination of qualities for someone who works with traumatized clients. I will explain why: Putting oneself forward as being faultless and denying one's shortcomings and mistakes, while at the same time lacking self-knowledge and lacking a desire to understand oneself better can mask a deeper self-doubt, and deep fears of intimacy and honesty. People with brain injuries need to feel secure around people who are open and honest in their reactions and feelings, given they can communicate this with empathy and respect. The client is best served by people who know their shortcomings and weaknesses, and thus are able to see their mistakes, learn from these mistakes and develop communicative competence. Those who wish to appear perfect use an inordinate amount of effort protecting their image at the expense of sensitivity to both their own inner life as well as the inner life of others. Counselling may help, but not always. Those who do not want to expose themselves to self-examination and deep reflection often choose to dismiss the psychologist's efforts as nonsense, unnecessary delving, making problems worse and a waste of money.

I will now proceed to justify the importance of recognising limitations. I have already dealt with the fact that a person, traumatised with a brain injury, is in need of help to manage insight as this will create better conditions for development. I have also claimed that the staff involved need self-insight and an open-mindedness attitude towards their own shortcomings and mistakes. I have even dared to state which kinds of people are unsuitable to work with cognitively disabled people. The natural follow-up question is: Which types of people are particularly suitable, in that case?

Those best suited to work with traumatised people see their own limitations and can be honest about this in relation to their colleagues and clients. This is the type of personality that is curious and eager to learn and who attempts to understand the clients' aims, their deeper intent, emotional needs, etc. This type is also curious about her own weaknesses, wants to understand her own needs and desires, can put up with feeling inadequate and helpless at times and still believe that it is possible to do something really meanwhile together with the client.

In my opinion, the clearest example of an inappropriate personality type is the medical staff who views brain damage as if it was an independent natural phenomena, which can only be influenced by chemical substances, and who means that the side effects are irrelevant since disabled people live such sheltered lives. I have met with staff who believes that side effects such as fatigue, obesity, acne, double vision, etcetera-etera, hardly matter. Who are of the opinion that depression, restlessness and physical symptoms related to the state of tension such as spasms and convulsions must be medicated at all costs. Who have an attitude to psychological methods as regards people with brain damage as «meaningless, it is a question of an organic brain injury!»

The most common attitude within neurological care is that brain damage causes abnormal mental and emotional patterns. Medication is the first choice should these symptoms need to be treated. A little counselling and a bit of advice to those around the patient about supporting memory and daily routines are also important. Recently, it has been discovered that rats' rehabilitation was improved when their environment is harmonic, so now we have evidence for this, too. In other words, environment is important. The fact that over the last 100 years, psychologists have built up an enormous knowledge bank on the effects of environmental influence, is of less importance. Biology is seen as the central discipline and psychology as an adjunct on the condition that psychologists do not bring up any controversial data that might question the authority of the doctor.

Some physicians consider psychologists and other health and care professionals as «Paramedical» staff. My colleague, Sigvard Lingh, suggested that we can respond to this by calling doctors «Parapsychological» staff ...

I wonder if there is any professional training other than the psychology program, where one must learn the importance of realizing one's own ignorance in relation to the patients. When will the doctor program teach this? I would like a nationally implemented health care which respects humanistic, philosophical, sociological and psychological research that deals with psychology and biology as equal disciplines in our joint task of exploring human life and existence. In fairness, and with gratitude, I can say that this attitude can be found among medical staff as well! Sometimes only in theory but many times in practice, too. I have talked to a number of doctors about the need for deep psychological expertise in healthcare, and most agree. However, in practice, most of them behave according to the medical routines they learned during their training. There is research that shows the influence of psychology on neurobiology and how people's perception of a situation affects them deeply, even the DNA molecules, which means that parts of the genome are affected by the environment.

Sigmund Freud sensed this long before modern research methods could verify his suppositions. Sigvard Lingh quotes Freud: «let the neurologists go in their direction, and we in ours. We will meet in a hundred years.» Lingh writes: «In the preface to the Swedish edition of Antonio Damasios' book *Descartes' error* (1994), Irene Matthis, MD, a psychoanalyst and Markus Heilig, associate professor of experimental psychiatry and senior consultant, wrote about this meeting. Collaboration between psychoanalytic and neurophysiologic researchers has already been established, and, in 1999, the first issue of a new international journal, *Neuro-Psychoanalysis*, with Antonio Damasio in the journal's scientific reference group was published» (Lingh, 2010).

Many attempts at bridging the gap between psychoanalysis and neuroscience have been made in recent years. Jaak Panksepp and Alan Schore, much quoted and cited researchers in the field of neuropsychoanalysis, both emphasize the importance of early relationships for the states of affect and mind in later years (Schore, 1994), (Panksepp, 1998).

So, on a DNA level, the genome is influenced by psychosocial stimulation. Ernest Rossi has described how this can be possible, in a number of articles and a couple of books. His theories are extremely detailed and his vocabulary demands some acquaintance with neurobiology. Rossi states that it is during moments of strong pressure, stress, or panic that the psycho-biological influence is greatest. Such episodes are often called traumatic as they can cause a mental trauma. Acute critical moments are «state bound», which means that we are conditioned or programmed to use acute survival strategies not only during the traumatic episode but in every episode thereafter, if the context has enough similarities with the original trauma. Such reminding contexts trigger the same state of mind as in the trauma. In the traumatic episode, the state of stress can last up to 2 hours. If, within this timeframe, one has the opportunity of intervening and influencing the person's perception of her condition, psychologically, with calm and confidence, one can usually prevent the development of Post Traumatic Stress Syndrome, PTSD[6]. If this is not possible, PTSD symptoms in some form will usually occur (Rossi, 2005/2006).

Rossi's conclusions are sometimes seen as being a little speculative. However, his ideas are not new and he makes references to other academic research. That the genome is partly plastic and receptive was demonstrated most clearly and thoroughly by the Nobel Prize winner, Kandel. Rossi's theories are well supported in Kandel's research, which is widely known and recognized (Kandel, 2001). I think that Rossi's crucial contribution has been to draw conclusions and present theories about how state-bound learning can be utilized therapeutically, not least through hypnosis.

The most common symptom of Posttraumatic stress disorder, PTSD, is that the raw experience of horror returns repea-

6 PTSD is a syndrome diagnosis that is used if, A) symptom aetiology is that the person has experienced, witnessed or been confronted by an event or events that involved death or serious injury (or threat thereof), or a threat to one's own or others' physical integrity. The individual reacted either with helplessness or horror. B) Common symptoms: recurrent, intrusive and distressing memories, thoughts, perceptions and / or nightmares related to the event. A feeling of reliving the experience. Intense distaste when confronted with anything that reminds one of an aspect of the traumatic experience. C) Persistent avoidance of stimuli associated with the trauma. This can include places, thoughts, conversations, memories, activities, and people. An inability to feel love and hope for the future. D) Two or more of the following symptoms: insomnia, irritability or outbursts of anger, difficulty in concentrating, excessively vigilant, and easily startled. E) The disorders (symptoms in B, C and D) have lasted for more than a month. F) The disorders cause clinically significant distress or impairment in social, occupational or other important respects. PTSD is classed as chronic if the symptoms persist for more than three months. Source: MINI-D IV. Diagnostiska kriterier enligt DSM. 1995. Danderyd: Pilgrim Press.

tedly in so-called flashbacks. One relives a state of panic, but one doesn't always «know» that what one feels is something that has already happened, much earlier. It is rather as if it is happening right now. Flashbacks can also appear in dreams, one wakes up because of the dream and feels and acts as if in the trauma. One can, thus, feel threatened with exactly the same stress as then and with the same panic. One is in the same state of mind as during the trauma. So, when you have reason to believe that a person's panic may be due to a flash-back, which, per definition, is state-bound, trauma-treatment is worth a try. During flash-backs, the person is in great need of help, support, and comfort and need to be embraced by people who can verbally explain what has happened and re-assure her that it is not happening now, that it is a memory. It happened then, not now. Since the flashback occurs in a state of timelessness, the therapist has a wonderful chance to be able to «be present in the patient's past» and provide support that wasn't available at the time. This kind of trauma work is common in psychotherapy with hypnosis and often docu-mented in the literature of dissociation, trauma and hypnosis. My own teachers on the subject included Onno van der Hart, Helen and John Watkins and Claire Frederick. Van der Hart has become known for his research on trauma, and dissocia-tion as a defence mechanism. Involuntary re-experiencing is typical for PTSD, and the flashbacks occur in collision with avoidance defence mechanisms. Symptoms of avoidance are memory loss and repression of certain thoughts and feelings as well as avoiding situations associated with the trauma (van der Hart, 2006).

Watkins and Frederick have developed a method based on psychodynamics known as Ego-State Therapy[7], where

7 «Ego State Therapy» is an approach taken to Sweden by Susanna Carolus-son within the framework of the Swedish Association of Clinical Hypnosis' psychotherapy program. The group of Swedish teachers has retained the English words «Ego State», because the literal translation to Swedish is rather clumsy.

the traumatised and dissociated part of the individual can be reached via hypnosis, imagery and focusing techniques (Watkins, 1997). It has similarities with hypnoanalysis, Guided Imagery, Internal Family Systems Therapy, Gestalt Therapy, psychodrama and «Parts Therapy».

Thus, there is a solid, overall clinical experience in the field, which is a qualitative form of evidence. The American Psychological Association, which is often used as an authority on psychological practice, defines clinical evidence as «the integration of the best available research with clinical expertise in the context of patient characteristics, culture, and preferences» (APA, 2006:273).

Philosophical and human sciences have always recognized well-documented clinical experience, while biological researchers have preferred experimental evidence. I am therefore grateful that colleagues such as Rossi spent time and effort developing the theory of curative factors, thus integrating clinical experience and neurological science in detail. I admire his efforts to explain the foundation and structure of the healing moments in clinical hypnosis at a neurobiological level.

REFERENCES

APA (2006) Evidence-Based Practice in Psychology. *American Psychologist. (61)* 271-275.

Kandel, E. (2001) The molecular biology of memory storage: A dialogue between genes and synapses. *Science, 295,* 1030-1038.

Klonoff, P. (2010) *Psychotherapy after Brain injury. Principles and techniques.* New York: The Guilford Press.

Lingh, S. (2010) *Psykopater och sociopater - ett spektrum.* Recito förlag.

Panksepp, J. (1998) *Affective neuroscience. The foundations of human and animal emotions.* New York: Oxford University Press.

Rossi, E. (2005/2006) Prospects for exploring the molecular-genomic foundations of therapeutic hypnosis with DNA microarrays. *American Journal of Clinical Hypnosis, 48* (2-3), 165-182.

Van der Hart (2006) *The Haunted Self: Structural Dissociation and the Treatment of Chronic Traumatization.* New York: W.W. Norton.

Schore, A. (1994) *Affect Regulation and the Origin of the Self.* Hillsdale: Lawrence Erlbaum Associate.

Watkins, J. & Watkins, H. (1997) *Ego States Therapy and Therapy.* New York: W. W. Norton.

CONVERSATION LEADING TO INSIGHT

Painted by Tobias in art therapy

The previous chapter was concerned with the importance of realizing ones limitations. That insight of this kind can lead to a better self-esteem and development seems paradoxical. And it is not without risks. One can only be aware of one's limitations if one is aware of one's merits as well. This is of fundamental importance if insight is to be of use. Elsewhere in this book, I have described how insight on shortcomings, without a sense of personal worth, can crush an individual, leading to escapism, anger, paranoia, delusions and halluci-nations. I will therefore give an example of how insight about shortcomings can be balanced by reinforcing the individual's feeling of worth.

This conversation all starts with a radio programme about alcoholism that inspires us to try an imaginative (hypnosis) exercise, followed by a cognitive exercise in math skills.

The psychological theory in support of my behaviour in the following example can be found in Winnicott's texts concerning the significance of play. Pretending games are extremely important for children's mental development, and the development of identity (Winnicott, 1981). The difference between pretence and hallucination is subtle and the ability to differentiate between the two develops during the first years of childhood. When Tobias was four years old, he pointed his toy gun at a friend of mine when she visited us. She reacted by saying that one should never point a gun at anyone. He told her directly that «this isn't a real gun, it's imaginary». When my 3 year old granddaughter wanted to ride on my back like on a horse, I told her that the floor was too hard for my knees and it hurt. She told me she would fix it, and proceeded to pretend to put knee protectors on my knees. I then told her that the pain in my knees was real and that I needed real knee protectors, not imaginary ones. She gave me a questioning look then accepted this fact. However, the ability to distinguish between inner (imagined) and outer reality can be lost in the case of traumatic brain injury. In my opinion, however, it is possible to regain this ability, the ability to distinguish between inner (imagination, hallucination) and outer reality. The following example is an illustration of this.

So, it's a radio programme that inspires us. Tobias starts thinking about his own situation and we start talking about it. This is followed by a supportive exercise that I shall soon describe and we finish the talk with a cognitive exercise which acts as proof of Tobias' ability to learn things. This is what happened:

It is Saturday morning and we are listening to a female alcoholic who describes her journey away from addiction. I say as I have said before:

«You might perhaps have become an alcoholic if your accident hadn't happened. You were drunk several times a week.»

«Maybe, don't know,» is Tobias answer.

The voice on the radio continues. She is describing how her addiction had got to the point where she was suffering from hallucinations; delirium. «I could see snakes hanging from the lamp in the ceiling,» she said.

Tobias comments:

«Me too.»

Hmm, I think. We must talk about this. It's a question of striking while the iron is hot, of taking the opportunity to enhance his self-knowledge and insight. I turn down the radio.

We talk a bit about hallucinations and imagination; what, in fact, is the difference between the two? How does one know whether something is just imagination? How does one know when something is an inner image, and not a tangible phenomenon that can be experienced by other people? Tobias suggests that he can't tell the difference.

I say the following sentence. I say it slowly with pauses between words. Read it in this way, please.

«I can imagine a snake on the table now.»

I describe the snake in detail. Tobias looks at the table in fascination.

«It's imaginary, though. How do I know that? Yes, because I can lift the snake up one meter in the air, I can move it to the left or right in my imagination. The snake is a figment of my imagination, then.»

I point to the table in front of us, it is a tangible object.

«The table, then? It is tangible. It's there ... Of course, I can imagine it a meter up in the air or to the left or to the right, but at the same time I can see the table on the floor. The table that is still there on the floor is the outer reality. I can't let my hand pass through it. It stops it, it is hard, and it really is there.

If I imagine the table up in the air, I can also move my hand through it. The table is created by my imagination.

If I close my eyes, the snake is as real as when my imagination created it on the table.»

Tobias spontaneously shuts his eyes.

«Me, too.»

«Can you see the snake when you close your eyes?»

«Yes.»

«It's not real, it's your imagination. Interesting?»

«Yes.»

«Is it civilized?»

«Mmm, almost.»

«Can you lift it up with your eyes?»

«Yes.»

«May I talk with it? I will talk to the snake and you can see how it reacts.»

I keep an eye on Tobias, of course, to see how he reacts when I talk to the snake. This is an ego-strengthening communication.

«Dear little snake, you are the sort that people are often afraid of. They think you are dangerous. But, you're Tobias' friend. You're only dangerous when you're afraid. You don't need to be afraid with Tobias, though. He will protect you. He can stroke you so you'll be completely calm. When you are harmonious with Tobias, you are a very nice, pleasant and cosy snake.»

Tobias looks pleased.

«You can lie at home on Tobias' sofa and wait for him to come home on Sunday evening. He'll look after you.»

We continue our conversation about the differences between reality and imagination. I conclude that it is called psychosis when he believes that the imagined is everyday reality and doesn't believe what other people see and hear. He agrees. I also add that a person who lives close to psychosis also has a high degree of creativity. When entering and leaving his world of fantasy is an act of his own will, it can be used in his art, when he paints.

He then reminds me that he can't always tell the difference between fantasy and reality. I ask him if this has happened recently. It is only obvious to me when Tobias is clearly confused or psychotic. Yes, it has been like this over the last week. This week, Tobias has had a relatively new assistant. She is a pleasant young woman of his own age, so he has had good reason to retreat from reality and let his imagination take over. Not quite intentionally, of course, as this defence mechanism is unconscious. If it was consciously chosen, he would also be consciously aware of the terrible and unbearable aspect of reality from which he is escaping, and if so, he could even talk about this to those around him. Not like now, this week, when those around him, assistants and family, have noticed a lack of concentration, an inability to listen and a generally confused state. But, as I have shown, we managed to help him retreat from his close-to-psychosis state. It didn't need much more than giving him a little help to identify the problem, namely the pain of having to receive help from a woman who, earlier, he might have tried to seduce with good grounds for success.

This is the reason Tobias was close to psychosis this week.

Our conversation continues with practical implications. Is it because of hallucinations that Tobias has left home and walked out at night in search of help from his brother? He answers «yes». Can it be that he awakens at night and sees snakes or other horrible things and believes that they are real? He answers yes to this question, too.

«Though ... almost know ... Thinking.»
    «Aha, so now you're thinking: Is this a fantasy or is it reality?»
    «Yes.»
    «When you phoned me once at half past three in the morning, was this one of those times?»
    «Yes.»
    «You were afraid of something you'd seen and needed someone to talk to?»
    «Yes.»
    «And it helped to talk a little while with me on the phone, so that you came back to reality?»
    «Yes.»
    «Good thing you phoned then!»

I bring the conversation back to the subject of a rich imagination as a resource.

«What an interesting autumn you're going to have. Art School on Wednesdays, you'll be able to make use of your imagination there, partly.»

I remind myself that the Art is an educational program, and that they give marks, so it will be a large portion of listening, attending to instructions, and technical rules for different forms of drawing and painting. How is it? Can he make use of instructions? Sometimes yes, sometimes no.

I praise him for at least trying; that he is prepared to listen and try new techniques in order to find out what suits him and can be used when painting, or what to refuse if he feels it doesn't suit his way of expressing himself.

I praise him for listening and learning, since he had difficulties with this before the accident, despite the fact that his left brain hemisphere was intact, and he had a greater capacity to understand instructions. Even then, he had a strong desire to learn from within his own motivation and curiosity.

I also mention the computer course that contains a certain amount of art since it involves Tobias downloading art works and saving them in a folder, as well as pasting in comments.

On Fridays, «Grunden» (which means ground, template and foundation - the name of an institute in the Community habilitation). Tobias has only been there a few times, and new phenomena are usually difficult to remember, so I describe the place a little. He then shows me by hand gestures how he walks over the hill in his living area, when he leaves his flat, thus letting me know that he understands what I am talking about. I say that there are nice people there, with interesting tasks, as I have been told by Tobias himself and his assistants. However, I know that new groups of people can make him restless and insecure. He usually wants to go to Brännö, then. I take the opportunity of preparing him for the autumn by saying that Fridays are work days for all of us; me, Tore, and Tobias. Brännö will be available on Friday evening at the earliest.

I continue talking about the advantages of Grunden. That Tobias can probably get the chance of working with animated film during the autumn and that a project of this kind is being prepared. This will give Tobias even larger artistic freedom! Great!

He smiles in recognition. We talked about this in June, and now it is August and he remembers.

Good.

Finally, I mention Tobias' third weekly activity: Vasa Primary School. One or two days a week, Mondays and maybe Tuesdays, Tobias will take part in the first or second classes in order to partake of their writing, reading and mathematics lessons. Primary School. Tobias has been doing this unusual activity over the past few years, reading and writing with the seven-year olds.

The mathematics will combine his powerful imagination, allowing him to think in images and amounts, with his brain's left hemisphere's ability to name numbers. Tobias starts counting out loud spontaneously like this: At the same time as he says «one» he writes «1» in the air. The writing comes first with the word coming a second later. He continues up to 40 and then I ask him for the next ten and he says 44. I tell him that he is thinking pictorially, and that I had asked him for the next «ten» and now he writes 50 in the air and then says it.

I congratulate him on his concentration and progress.

His eleventh year after the accident has shown that he has not only gained insight, self-confidence, alertness and presence of mind but he has also progressed in purely cognitive skills.

REFERENCE

Winnicott, D. (1981) *Lek och Verklighet*. Stockholm: Natur & Kultur. In original: Playing and Reality. London: Tavistock Publications, 1971.

I ALSO WANT TO HAVE CHILDREN!

Tobias nephew is now one year old. Recently, It became clear to me that last year's crisis, in connection with his sister-in-law's pregnancy and his brother's fatherhood, the week of the birth and the period that followed, threatened not only Tobias' hope of an own family in the future , but also and to higher degree made Tobias jealous. He lives in a timeless existence, moving through a variety of ages. He was small, our firstborn, the one who jealously threw a toy car at the baby stroller with his little brother inside, when all their cousins gathered around the newborn boy. Tobias regressed then, to being unable to walk, only crawl, despite his two years and four months. He regressed now as well, owing to a similar fear of losing our love. When I guessed that he missed having a family of his own, he replied with emphasis that I was wrong and that it was all about fear that we would love the baby more and forget about him. We, that is my husband Tore, and I.

Four weeks later and with Wille four weeks older, Tobias has discovered Wille's charm and has begun to appreciate him, exactly as he did with his little brother once.

And, just the other day he said that he would like to have a child himself.

We, Tore, Tobias and I, were sitting on the veranda in the sunshine eating a peaceful Sunday breakfast. We had plenty of time to carefully talk about the question of whether Tobias could manage a child despite his serious disability. He pointed to his genitalia, meaning that he is fully capable. Which was not exactly what we meant, of course. He saw no difficulties, his arm is getting better and better, so carrying and changing nappies etcetera would be no problem.

We listened. We asked questions. We didn't press him. Reality will catch up with him in time. The fact that we don't encourage the illusion about having a family of his own, that we express a cautious doubtfulness is quite enough to sow seeds of doubt in Tobias. More than this is unnecessary; he sees our doubts and he will swallow this frustrating reality when he has the strength to understand how his disability hinders parental responsibility.

With this example I make the point that insight cannot be forced upon anyone, especially someone in a vulnerable state. Insights into his lost hopes about parenthood will come, eventually, if he takes up the subject again. He will show when he is willing to hear doubts and when he is prepared to face the fact that his disability creates problems for parenthood.

The balance between empathetic support and realistic confrontation can seem difficult. However, if one is steered by concern and respect, intuitive listening can show us how fast or slow to go. We don't say: «No, Tobias, you will never be able to become a father, just face the fact!» Neither do we say: «Yes, wouldn't it be lovely if you had your own family!»

Perhaps the reader finds both of these alternatives absurd? That no one can take away from anyone, least of all brain-damaged disabled persons, their dreams of a better future? Or that one must never allow someone who cannot possibly look after a child to have unrealistic dreams about it? I bring this question up because I have met people who work in the care sector who directly bring people down to earth without any feeling or respect for how and when such a confrontation should be made. It is possible that these people carry their own unprocessed disappointments that come to the surface when other people express longings and dreams. Unintentionally and unknowingly, they transfer their own frustration onto people who cannot defend themselves or question their words.

I have also seen staff play some kind of make-believe where anything is possible, dreams are encouraged and any realistic objections from team colleagues are written off as being humourless and dull. The people with this kind of attitude seem to see the person with a brain-injury as having no memory at all and having no need to face facts.

A walk with nephew Tova

It is not meant in a bad way, when members of staff «play» with the client by encouraging dreams and future visions that have no real chance of becoming reality. It is probably more a question of ignorance, a lack of reflection or a personal habit of relating to life. Maybe the person in question handles life's disappointments by dreaming about a future that is not in any way possible. It may also be a way of fending off, of avoiding having to confront the patient in a realistic and serious manner.

This is why staff training and regular psychological consultation is necessary.

APHASIA AND THE ART OF DIALOGUE

Tobias is not fully aware of his injuries. I am impressed though by just how much understanding he does cope with.

It's probably very hard to cope with the facts. How can he possibly manage to realise that there is a whole world of words, thoughts, verbal exchange and insights that, at one time were part of his daily life, but from which he is now partly excluded, and cannot participate in as fluently as he used to? How does it feel to see a group of people interrelate about something he doesn't fully understand, in a language he doesn't command, and with a verbal participation that he has had, but has lost? Tobias sees the social intercourse, and seems to try to be the person he used to be, when he could take part in what is now a more or less perplexing interplay. Earlier, he could really enjoy having a discussion; now he pretends as well as he can. Sometimes he truly enjoys it, but at other times he just acts as if he does, while at times he exaggerates so that he goes too far.

Today, he was really stubborn and tireless in his attempts at making himself understood. I was at Tobias' flat along with his assistant, Anders. I asked him if an old school mate had given him a phone call this week. The reason I asked was because this old school mate, Kristina Bergman, had phoned me to ask if I thought it would be suitable to give Tobias a call and suggest going out for a cup of coffee. She had been reminded about him when she saw a news feature on the TV about Tobias taking part in his old primary school. Oh, yes, she had phoned, he was sure of it. I, on the other hand, was doubtful. Her name ought to have been forgotten by now, so how could I know whether he really understood who I meant?

Yes, he was certain and said «two». I guessed that he meant that they went to the same school in the second class. Yes, this is so, and he tried to explain something. He drew two circles in the air and said the word «four». Two circles and the word «four». Hmm. Did he mean class four? No, not that. Perhaps four meant some span of time - that they were to meet in four days? No. In four weeks, then? No. Perhaps it was four friends that were going to meet each other? No. I took a backward step with my guesses and asked Tobias if he meant an amount when he said «four». Once again he answered, no. I was beginning to wonder if he really knew what he was talking about. Was this really about Kristina Bergman or had he changed subjects? It often happens that we think he has got an opinion about something we're talking about, when in fact he has not been listening to us, he's been thinking about something else, and then suddenly wants to talk about it. Or, it might be that he gets a thought about what we are talking about but his attempt to express himself is so subjective that we haven't a chance of understanding his associations.

We assumed in this case that it was Kristina he was talking about. Tobias' assistant, Anders, and I made wild guesses. Tobias looked tired and frustrated. He repeated «four» and showed four fingers that he held tight into each other, which seemed to be significant. I wondered if he meant a family of four people. No.

He made gestures for hills or high waves or whatever it was that he drew in the air. He repeated «here» and «there» and pointed around a little. Then the high round forms again. I suddenly got an image of hills, buildings and cities.

«Do you mean cities?»

«Yes!»

«A city with a name with four letters?»

«Yes!»

I guessed at Lund and Umeå, but no.

Andres guessed Oslo, and Tobias breathed out, relieved.

We understood that Kristina Bergman, or whoever the caller was, apparently lived in Oslo, or had lived there.

It was now easier to see what Tobias was trying to show us in order to communicate the word «Oslo». Here and there. «There» is our holiday paradise, the Norwegian mountains, pointing around meant that we used to drive around or through Oslo on our way to the mountains.

A few weeks later I found out that the person who had contacted Tobias was another childhood friend, who lives or stays in Oslo and who had called after seeing Tobias on TV; Paola.

THE FAILURE OF SHORT TERM MEMORY

2008 11 22
Frihet från ep+ran/oill

«Freedom from epilepsy», drawing by Tobias

I am at Tobias' flat, and it is not like when he is with us on Brännö. When he is with us, he is served all meals by whoever is cooking, usually Tore. I now want to find out how well Tobias manages by himself. I am sitting on the sofa in the living room while Tobias gets on with making breakfast for us both in the kitchen. He works best when I am not in sight, but in easy reach should he need help. When he decides that breakfast is ready, he has got as far as pouring out two glasses of orange juice, opened two cartons of yogurt, and two boiled eggs are lying on the kitchen table. Cheese and butter, cheese cutter and butter knife are laid out, too. He has taken out two tea cups, but is in the process of putting them back again. He has really tried, because he's done a good job! I ask him for permission to take out some salads and whether there is any bread. He finds the bread and puts four slices onto a plate. We make sandwiches and sit down to table. I ask aloud if there is anything missing. It takes Tobias 20 minutes to find an egg-cup. He has only one, so every time he opened the cupboard where this eggcup was in sight, the number didn't match with whatever he was looking for, probably. I finally solve the problem by saying that he can use the eggcup and I will manage with a schnapps glass or my wedding ring.

We eat peacefully, and it is almost ten o'clock. As I know that he likes to drink tea for breakfast I ask him if he'd like to make a cup, and, yes, he'd like that. He makes tea in a pot with no difficulty. He then goes to the refrigerator to get some milk but comes back empty-handed. The milk was finished and he has no thoughts about how to solve the problem. He's not thinking now, which he might well have done if he'd been alone. I ask him if he wants to drink tea without milk today or whether he wants to make the effort of going and buying some. Tobias gets up straight away, as milk is usually important for him. Just as he's going out the door I call «It's milk you want!» I'm not certain he heard me, though. The supermarket lies right across the road, but he is gone for 30 minutes, and when he returns, what has he bought? A package of disposable plastic cups, and a packet of plastic spoons. When I point out his mistake he tells me that he needs these, too. I propose that we go back to the shop together, and he agrees.

Tobias is a regular in the supermarket. He goes up to the cashier, points at his head and says «cuckoo». She replies «You got it wrong, did you?» I explain what went wrong, and things get sorted out. When we come home with the milk, I decide that it is important to understand Tobias' thinking process here, as it is seldom «cuckoo». There is always some kind of logic even if it seems crazy. We finally work out that his thoughts were still on the problem with the eggcups. He had forgotten all about buying milk, but knew he was in the shop for some reason, for something he needed, so he looked around all the supermarket aisles hoping to see something that would offer him a clue … What captured his attention, maybe because they could be associated to eggcups and breakfast, were disposable plastic mugs and spoons. They were far too large for the purpose, but for the sake of saving face he had to come home with something …

Can one live like this and still be happy? Yes, it is a mystery but he does. He is so conscious yet so forgetful. He has no tools for retrieving memory. He is so damaged! And yet, he lives alone in his flat, with the help of assistants of course, but still … He is well-known in the neighbourhood and most people believe he copes better than he actually does. I cannot really understand it. He is worth respect, awe and love. I just wish he could find someone to love. How can he find a woman, a woman he can respect and be respected by, and who is clever enough to understand his highly subjective idiom/language?

SECONDARY TRAUMATIZATION

Counsellor and psychotherapist, Lill Molén, has written a paper on secondary traumatisation. The term means that a person related to someone who has suffered traumatic damage or loss will also be traumatised (Molén, 2005). The use of the word «secondary» is not the same as in the diagnostic expression «secondary depression», where the word secondary refers to further symptoms occurring in one and the same person. Secondary traumatisation is all about the compassion of close relatives. I suffer from secondary traumatisation. Why not primary? From my own subjective perspective, I feel myself to be primary traumatised.

However, the term «secondary» does serve a special function. It shows that those who «are untouched» by the trauma that has affected their close relative, are in fact very touched by it.

Not only relatives are affected by secondary traumatisation, health-care staff is also affected. Therapists see secondary traumatisation as one of the aspects of counter transference. It is called «compassion fatigue», a sort of surrogate traumatisation; one carries someone else's pain (Stamm, 1997). In order to deal with counter transference of this kind, one needs to distinguish one's own pain from the pain one receives from the other person. Supervisors and psychodynamically oriented psychotherapists are attentive to the caregivers' need to discriminate between their own various reactions and feelings. Emotional reactions in staff can emanate from personal associations and feelings, or from subjective empathy with a client, or from identification with the client by projection, i.e. contagion and transferred denied affect from the client onto the staff. This kind of psychological supervision prevents staff members from mixing up one's own feelings with those of others. It is an art one can practise and learn. Empathy and compassion can eventually become an asset rather than drainage. As early as the 1970s, Carl Rogers said that the role of the therapist is to «perceive the client himself as he is seen by himself, to lay aside all perceptions from the external frame of reference while doing so, and to communicate something of this empathic understanding to the client.» (Rogers, 1951, p. 29).

Ciaramicoli and Ketcham define empathy as «the ability to understand and respond to another person's unique experience» (Ciaramicoli & Ketcham, 2000, p. 14). If helping professions need only that, our competence would be nothing but understanding clients. However, empathy is just a part of the therapeutic interaction. What is perceived as empathy by the caregiver herself may be contaminated with countertransference in Freud's original meaning. It means that the therapist's emotional reactions, even when perceived as empathy, do not always reflect the client's experience. They can be activated by interactional patterns from the therapist's early relations. These early patterns affect how the therapist interprets and reacts to the client. I define and discuss this kind of transference in greater depth in Psykologtidningen (Carolusson, 2004).

One of my earlier students in psychotherapy, Pär Ekström, wrote his academic examination paper on the topic secondary traumatisation. He started out from the general experience that the symptoms are almost identical to those of PTSD, posttraumatic stress disorder. Ekström's source is Bride, 2003 (Ekström, 2005). The psychologist Sigvard Lingh, reminded me that the PTSD diagnosis was not really recognized until it was presented in the diagnostic manual, «DSM-III», 1980. Since then, the use of the diagnosis has dramatically increased, especially for U.S. soldiers involved in various wars around the world. Between 2002 and 2008, more than 230 000 soldiers have been diagnosed with PTSD following time served in Iraq or Afghanistan (Lingh, 2010).

On Tuesday, the 31st of October, 2008, I phone to Tore, who is working at home, to ask him to give me some information from the computer. While Tore is speaking quietly with me, I hear something in the background; Tore speaks to someone and I understand that Tobias is there. It is a Tuesday, a normal working day for Tobias as well. Which means that he is psychotic. This is my first thought, since it would take a great deal for the assistants to break the weekly schema, and leave Tobias to us on a Tuesday. They know that we need weekdays to be able to get on with earning our living. So, even if Tobias should suggest Brännö midweek, there is a silent agreement that since we are with him from Friday afternoon to Sunday afternoon, we need our own time in between. Anyway, I hear Tore say:

«Take the pill now. No! Not on the floor!»
Then to me:
«Tobias is here.»
«Yes, I hear that. Is he crazy?»
«Yes.»

I have one more client to see, today. I must concentrate. Luckily, I have the knack of distinguishing between professional life and private life, and the ability to exist in different ego states or roles, in other words, a sort of dissociation within the compass of constructive coping. I can formulate my attitude to my work as follows:

They pay for my services with money, commitment, time and confidence. No matter whether it is counselling, teaching, or psychotherapy, they have a right to my full concentration. It is not only the question of a sense of duty, it is also a meaningful and moral point of view with which I feel comfortable and «in sync». Only for a moment did the thought of Tobias pop up in my mind during the therapy session, and I pushed it away immediately.

It was more difficult going home on the tram. I was restless, worried and in that no-man's-land of feeling the weight of distress within someone close, when they are somewhere else. I can neither see, hear, nor feel anything that can guide me in my worries. I just have my fear-ridden imagination to which I will not listen, as it is perfectly pointless. So I solve a Sudoku.

When the Sudoku is solved, I decide to concentrate on myself. I can't help Tobias and Tore, anyway, sitting there on the tram and boat. What do I feel? I feel fear, a primitive fear. I recognize it, my body remembers Tobias' distress, and it remembers my empathy with Tobias' psychotic anxiety from all the previous episodes. How can anxiety be so infectious?

Have my mirror neurons[8] absorbed the anxiety that Tobias has exuded? My brain absorbs the anxiety, while Tobias makes himself unaware of it; he projects it onto his environment, smashes everything into fragments and goes crazy. I receive his feelings and contain them for him since he himself can't. Within psychotherapy, this phenomenon is called projective identification: He projects his unbearably impossible-to-carry feelings upon me, and I feel them and experience them as my own. When using the concept of projective identification, one makes the assumption that someone, actively but unconsciously, gets rid of something unbearable and dumps it onto the other. In a healing relationship, the receiver doesn't throw the feeling back, as is otherwise common in destructive relationships, where the projections will bounce back and forth in a destructive downward spiral. On the contrary, the professional therapist can hold onto the feeling, try to understand it and process it, choose a suitable time to interpret the feeling, and eventually make the feeling «digested», «reframed» and tolerable within the relationship. In the long run, the patient

---

8 The term mirror neuron refers to neurologist, Rizzolatti's discovery of local brain activity which corresponds to apes' and humans' ability to imitate the movements and the intended movement of others (Nilsson, 2009, page 101)

might be able to cope with the feeling herself, tolerating the experience of it and taking responsibility for how and whether to express it. Sandler has described the phenomenon thoroughly (Sandler, 1987), but Ogden is the most renowned authority in the literature on projection, identification, and projective identification (Ogden, 1977).

Sitting on the boat and not being with Tobias means that this cannot be a question of direct projective identification, so long as the projection isn't being transferred telepathically, but then we would be beyond the realms of psychology. Probably, it is a combination of my own pure anxiety and the activated memories of the many projections I have had from Tobias during earlier psychoses. I have had enough strength to carry the anxiety. I cannot go crazy, as I am hindered and protected by my maternal love and my parental responsibility. Besides, I have no brain damage, and I have no predisposition towards madness. Should I go over the border of reality, a flight from reality into madness, I would dissociate more; I would divide life up into parts, and deny those parts I cannot manage. I would perhaps act as if in a state of shock, mechanically, practically and with less anxiety than now. The anxiety wouldn't disappear, of course. A state like this invokes so much stress in the brain that the chain reaction of stress hormones, neuropeptides, the fight/flight response or playing-dead reaction must have an impact, a physical impact, experienced as anxiety. My body would suffer from the strain. It did 1997. During the first year after Tobias' accident, I had chronic urinary tract infections that no medication could cure until after six months.

So, I am sitting on the boat, avoiding somatic illness by accepting my feelings, or so I believe. I decide to cope by creating the idea that I feel like a worried hen. «Worried hen» are the words that spring to mind. Hen? Mother to its chicken. Exactly. If Tobias was my client, not my son, but somebody else's son, would I feel this anxiety? Would my involvement in his state, which I call projective identification, be so strong? No, I don't think so. I feel my anxiety. I want to cry, I want to scream «get me out of here! I don't want to be involved! Take it away, give us peace, give Tobias peace, and give Tobias back his soul!»

As if he was possessed.

Yes! I want to beg the spirit that is haunting him to go! No, this is wishful thinking. This isn't how it works. I have thought it out deeply, and it doesn't work. It is probably a question of secondary traumatisation in combination with empathy and projective identification.

If I react like this, despite being aware of what is going on, how, then, does it feel for relatives and staff who are affected by emotions, projections and anxiety, without having a clue about what is actually happening, on a deep psychological level?

Guidance and counselling supervision is necessary. Family support is necessary.

REFERENCES

Bride, B., Robinson, M., et al. (2003) Development and valida-tion of the Secondary traumatic Stress Scale. *Research on Social Work Practice. vol 13, 2003*, s.1-16. Sage Publications. Referred to in: Ekström, P. 2005.

Carolusson, S. (2004) Självkännedom minskar risken för mo-töverföring. *Psykologtidningen, 15.*

Ekström, P. State-dependent recall: Självskattning av sekun-där traumatisering hos behandlare. Uppsats psykoterapeut-examen maj 2005. Svenska Föreningen för Klinisk Hypnos. *www.hypnosforeningen.se*

Ciaramicoli, A. & Ketcham, K. (2000) *Empatins Makt. Hur man uppnår närhet, självinsikt och varaktig kärlek.* Stockholm: Bokförlaget Forum. In original: The power of Empathy. Penguin, Putnam. 2000.

Lingh, S. (2010) Personal communication.

Molén. L. (2005) Sekundär traumatisering. Trauma med fokus på behandlaren. Projektarbete Grundläggande Psykoterapiutbildning, Östersund, Psykiatriska kliniken, 2005-2007.

Nilsson, A. (2009) *Det omedvetna i nya perspektiv. Ett psykiskt system mellan hudens och känslans beröring.* Sthlm: Brutus Östlings Bokförlag Symposion.

Ogden, T. (1977) Projective Identification and Psychotherapeutic Technique. *www.amazon.com*

Rogers, C. (1951, 1965, 1973, 1976, 1979) *Client-centered Therapy. Its current practice, implications and theory.* London: Constable.

Sandler, J. (1987). The Concept of Projective Identification. *Bul. Anna Freud Centre, 10* p. 33-49.

Stamm, B. (1997) Work Related Secondary Traumatic Stress. *PTSD Research Quarterly. vol 8, nr 2.* The National Center for PTSD, US.

DESPAIR

Sunday the 29th of October 2007. I have worked both Saturday and Sunday. I have been teaching about psychoses, diagnostics and treatment. I travel home to Brännö and only manage to meet Tobias for an hour before it is time for him to return home to his flat.

That Sunday evening he is in good form, but at night, Tobias has a strong epileptic seizure. His bed is soaking wet and, according to his assistant, he sleeps until three o'clock in the afternoon on Monday. He wakes with a fever. The next morning when he awakens, his mouth is covered in a white substance. Perhaps he's been chewing toothpaste, or he has had another seizure and the white is dried froth. His assistant gets a hug that goes beyond what is respectful and Tobias wants to kiss him all over.

Tobias tries to work on the computer but he is totally consumed by his inner world and can't get anything done. He gets more and more restless. The assistant suggests a fast walk in the hope that exercise will help do something about the restlessness.

They go out in order to buy ink for the printer. Tobias is unaware of his surroundings; he bumps into people, and is lost in a world of his own. When they get back home, he doesn't follow the normal routine of taking his shoes off. The assistant asks him about it, and he replies that he intends to keep them on. The assistant then shows Tobias the receipt for the ink, as Tobias usually appreciates controlling his own economic status. The assistant asks Tobias where he should put the receipt.

It is easy to see, looking back, that this is a far too advanced task for Tobias in the state he was in. Tobias goes crazy and hits the assistant, who puts up with it for fifteen minutes until Tobias gives up and goes out through the door. The assistant directly phones to Mården, who drives to the nearby café and finds Tobias there. The owner of the café knows Tobias, as he is a frequent guest. When he is in this state, we now know that the feelings, or rather, affects[9], closest to the surface are (sexual) arousal, and anger, or fear, and that they are also very easily provoked into action. Tobias takes the hand of the café owner as if to kiss it, and then he bites her.

She becomes scared and screams. Mården takes Tobias away, phones to Tore who is on Brännö, and drives Tobias to the boat. Mården then returns to the café and explains the situation. Fortunately, the owner is very understanding. She has seen Tobias from his best sides many times earlier.

---

9 The concept of emotion is attributed to the child's perception of the environment when it has reached a certain level of experience and maturity, which is not true of affects. Affects is modern psychology's word for the child's inherent system of values (Nilsson, 2009). The early psychoanalytic «drive theory» counted on two biologically-rooted states of experience in the services of survival, namely, the pleasure and pain principle. When the concept «affect» was introduced into modern psychology, one had noticed that new-born children showed more nuances then pleasure and pain. According to Silvan Tomkins, referred to by Nilsson, affects are unconscious, bodily-rooted experiences of good and bad, pleasure and displeasure that are expressed in more nuances in the form of nine different inborn affects. These are the negative affects: fear, disgust, loathing anger, anguish and shame, and the positive affects: pleasure and interest. The ninth affect is surprise which I interpret as being neutral. These basic affects are experienced in relation to the environment and the parents who mirror and put words to the affects time and time again until the child matures and manages to retain the experiences so that they become feelings. Emotional experience is thus at an abstract and associative level that is as much mental as it is physical.

Things are much the same on Brännö. Tobias has a sandwich and some porridge, eats it, and then goes to the dishwasher to put in his plate. Tore tells him that the dishwasher is working, full of plates and dishes. Tobias is of a different opinion. Tore says that the dishwasher door shouldn't be opened now. (In retrospect, Tore realizes that he ought to have just let Tobias put the plate in the machine while it was working, and thus avoiding coming in conflict with Tobias.) Tobias tears the hatch open, climbs up on it with all his weight and smiles triumphantly, signalling «ha, ha, I was right».

The assistant phones and wants to talk about the day. He is shaken and upset, of course. He talks it over, for half an hour. He needs this as a kind of «debriefing», I guess. Despite the pressure, I listen happily as I am so thankful that the assistants put up with this primitive scenario, and don't just disappear – for good. Oh no, the assistant wants to meet Tobias as soon as possible so that they can be reconciled.

In the evening I sit at Tobias' bedside. He is ready for sleep. One can call it counselling, with the difference that he is my son, and I have no professional relationship to him. This is of no importance when it comes to someone with a brain injury, Tobias needs to feel that caring people help him with his feelings. That these people are family is not a disqualification, so long as the family member doesn't mix personal needs with Tobias' needs. In order to manage this distinction, it is a huge advantage or perhaps even a necessity, that I have the profession that I have.

I tell him how much we love him, and ask if he can understand this. No, he can't. His immediate denial verifies my theory that this state of confusion is not only a neurological lack of order, but also has a deeper cause in a lack of self-esteem, self-worth and self-respect.

Therefore, I ask him if he likes himself, which he also denies. I describe to him that, when he is hitting out, he demonstrates contempt. And that he despises himself. Tobias agrees. He listens carefully when I describe contempt as a defence mechanism. I describe how self-contempt is projected outwards, since it is unbearable to feel worthless. I make the connection with his injury, his difficulties, and how tired of it all he is. Tobias agrees. After a while he needs the toilet again, and when he returns he makes it quite clear that I should go. His gestures are intense and slightly contemptuous, so I guess that he is going to wander back and forth as he usually does in evenings when he feels like this.

To my huge relief, Tobias falls asleep and doesn't wake until half past eight next morning.

The next morning: I hear that Tobias has got up. He's in the bathroom. Laughing out loud. Yes, this is the next stage in the psychosis process. We have a certain amount of experience by now. I ask him directly whether he's got too much traffic in his head and to my relief he answers yes. This is good because I can motivate him to take medication, a Nozinan[10], which reduces agitation, mania, and anxiety, especially in a state of psychosis.

I ask him if he wants a tablet to cool things down in his head and he says yes. Then, he takes a shower and he can even take my advice about logistics as regards shampooing the hair, soap on the body, etcetera. Only at one point does he show irritation and, in order to avoid an escalation, I ask him immediately:

«You think I'm nagging you now?»

«Yes.»

«OK, I'll go out, you're getting on fine. Call if you want help with something.»

He is finished. I give him breakfast, and offer him a B-vitamin and a calcium tablet, which I take every day. At first he says yes, but then gets suspicious and says no. I say:

---

10 Levomepromazine in Germany and Methotrimeprazine in America (Sold as Nosinan, Nozinan, Levoprome)

«OK, you don't want one. I take one every day. I'll take mine now.»

«OK,» says Tobias and takes one as well.

Tore is going out and says goodbye, and goes up to Tobias. He pats him on the cheek. Tobias gets furious, looks at Tore with that contemptuous look and takes his hand away with violent force. Tore understands directly and says «Sorry» … «Sorry».

I stare at Tobias, I feel directly that he mustn't be allowed to use this contemptuous tone of voice. I try looking at Tore and say: «It's not you that should be saying sorry». Then I say to Tobias:

«It is quite normal for a father to pat his son's cheek.»

Tobias then says «sorry» in an honest way, but Tore is a bit quick in saying «Yes», and Tobias isn't satisfied and repeats in an increasingly aggressive manner:

«Sorry! Sorry! Sorry!!»

When he starts getting up and moves towards Tore with his «Sorry». I guess that he is working up another attack of anger and I say to him:

«Enough! You've been forgiven. It's not a big deal.»

He takes me seriously, he respects my words. Luckily. It may be because there are two of us around Tobias. He can point his anger at one of us and trust the other one.

After breakfast we talk. Tobias face is grey and his eyes are colourless. I tell him that he gets crazy when he can't put up with himself.

«You have big difficulties, it is awful, and everyone we know likes you so much.» We want to say: «Tobias, how can we help?» «Tobias, can we do something for you?»

Tobias looks carefully at me.

«And you want to answer: Yes, take my injury away; throw a spell so my brain is whole again!»

Tobias looks very carefully at me.

«But, we can't. We can't fix your brain. We can only support you to continue training, practising, struggling on as you do.

We admire your fortitude. You insist on learning to read, you paint, you are working at Grunden ... However, you have a right to have an off-day like today, when you're tired of life as it is. In order to avoid feeling these awful feelings, you get contemptuous and angry at us ... I want to help you stay well in your head. The truth: What you are feeling deep inside is what is going to keep you well. You need to have the strength to feel it. As it is.

What are you feeling right now? Are you disappointed ... angry ... or unhappy, or in despair, what do you feel? Honestly!!»

«Unhappy.»

«That was a brave thing to say. You're unhappy. Do you need to cry?»

«Yes.»

«You usually find it difficult to cry. Can you cry?»

«No ... It's enough now.»

«You want me to stop now, it's getting painful?»

«Yes.»

«OK.»

My thoughts:

I reach him, Tobias can almost feel his unhappiness, but it is too painful to feel fully. We take a break from our conversation. He wants to go to bed. I ask him if he wants a goodnight hug. Tobias says yes.

I sit on Tobias' bed. He shows that I must keep a distance. I see this, that just now, closeness is too difficult for him. I wonder why.

«What is so terrible about closeness?»

It looks as if Tobias is making an honest attempt at thinking, and answers just as honestly that he does not know.

I talk about earlier episodes when he has been in this sort of state, but has still enjoyed being hugged. He had allowed himself to feel like a one-year-old, to remember how it was to be small and hugged and secure. It was protection.

Not now, though. Time to go the toilet again. When he returns and goes into his room, I stand beside him in the doorway. Right there, in the doorway, he starts going towards me and it is obvious from his eyes that he wants to hit me. He steps forward in order to strike. I say sharply:

«You mustn't hit me!»

Tobias continues to come towards me and I back off. I don't have his physical strength so I must find words to stop him. I back off just out of reach. Then he stops when I say:

«Do you want to hit me?»

«Yes!»

«Yes, you want to, but you will not. You don't hit me and I don't hit you. I respect you.»

He breathes out and says:

«Good!»

His voice is still hard and distant, though. I continue to talk about our mutual respect. I can see he's listening, but I can't feel that we have contact.

«Do you still feel like hitting out?»

«Yes.»

«You can go to your room and hit the pillow, then.»

He looks inquiringly at me, showing plainly that there's no logic in this. Which is true, he wants to hurt, not just vent his frustration. I show him how one can hit the wall with one's fists.

«Some people hit the wall in order to cope with their anger.»

Tobias looks at me in wonder, with cold, grey eyes.

«You can manage to control your desire to hit out in your own way. You can do it!»

«Yes!» says Tobias in a tone of voice that says «ha-ha, I won!»

This psychosis goes under the title of «ha-ha, I won!» and «I don't need anyone, don't get close, 'cause I might explode, don't try to believe you can get through to me.»

Medication isn't enough. It suppresses the worst of his anguish and dampens restlessness, but it can't eliminate the underlying self-hate, the bottomless despair, and the death-wish. One can ask how I know this. Well, imagine yourself that you have an accident that results in the loss of your ability to read, write, remember, plan, find someone to date, look forward to a career or at least a job that you can be proud of, to have a family ... you realise that all of this is out of reach now, and maybe forever. Try living with these thoughts and feelings a short while. Most people think «I can't», some think «God, how awful, I wouldn't manage.» And some people perhaps can imagine how it in fact feels to realise the unbearable. «I'd go to pieces» – that is my feeling. «I just want to cry» is another possible feeling. But, if I cry and cry and cry, what happens then? Nothing is different, nothing is better. I just can't cry anymore. What then? No, this isn't possible. Can I flee from myself? Get drunk? Then what? A hangover I suppose, and more anguish, nothing has changed.

I understand Tobias, and yet I can't understand, because it is impossible. One can only flee. In Tobias' case, to anger and despair. When one doesn't want to live anymore one can die in triumph, hate, hate and rage, with no thought for the consequences, because everyone else can take them, when I'm gone. I don't care about the morrow; it isn't there for me anyway. You, who still have a life, if I hurt one or two of you, what does it matter? What is that suffering compared to mine?

This is how I understand Tobias' psychosis from a psychological, existential perspective.

The psychosis is understandable if we have the courage to see the profound fact that Tobias knows that he has lost an independent life and the terrible torment this is for him.

Another night has passed. This morning, Tore went to the office. I am alone with Tobias. I make preparations for meeting any possible aggressiveness when Tobias wakes up. Respect, praise, and encourage him while at the same time, in order to counteract his contempt, tell him how hard he's suffering so that, hopefully, he can receive aid in being confirmed in his pain.

In order to meet the psychotic Tobias, I must have full presence, and full identification, not with his defence, but with the underlying feelings that he hates to feel.

When Tore set off, he said to me that we are beginning to create good routines for meeting these situations.

I answered, yes, but added: At the same time, it is getting more and more painful for me each time.

It is like a civil war. When the fighting is over, one breathes out and is overjoyed about living peacefully with one's neighbours and one has found new ways of cooperating. One enjoys the peace and manages to be normal and in harmony again. Then the minority starts to mistrust again, they are the downtrodden, the robbed, the terrorists. A new attack comes; snipers stalk, enjoying their vengeance. Now one must fend them off again, find survival strategies, or even better, outwit the terrorists, and persuade them to stop fighting and dare to believe in a peaceful coexistence.

To suffer a brain injury corresponds to the oppression and disadvantage that terrorists hate, and that awakens jealousy, contempt, rage and a need for revenge. Revenge is fuelled by a longing for justice and restoration which is impossible in Tobias' case since the unjust accident is irreversible.

In the middle of the day, Tobias takes a Nozinan and then watches TV. A replay of Doobidoo11. Celebrities compete in a quiz, the linkman, Lasse Kronér, is really funny and now they're singing «Lassie» and laughing. Tobias catches my attention and explains that he is the «Lassie» they're singing about. When I say that for me he is Tobias, he repeats intensively that he is Lassie. It is not as if he wants to tell me something, or explain a feeling or an experience. By now, I can

11 A Friday evening entertaining musical family TV program in Sweden.

recognise Tobias' body language when it is a question of an escape from reality. Tobias has a wonderful idea about being someone else, some fantastic creature that they sing about on TV, and if he can get me to realise this then all anguish, all despair, and all this terrible stuff that really must disappear, will be gone. He'll be back to normal and it's wonderful.

However, I cannot agree. I say:

«Hmm, I don't really understand this.»

Tobias says:

«But it's true!»

«Ok, maybe for you, you understand this, but I don't. We'll just have to leave it at that!»

He relaxes and contents himself with this.

REFERENCE

Nilsson, A. (2009) *Det omedvetna i nya perspektiv. Ett psykiskt system mellan hudens och känslans beröring.* Sthlm: Brutus Östlings Bokförlag Symposion.

THE LOGIC OF A PSYCHOSIS

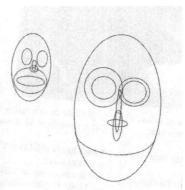

It is three days since the psychosis broke out on Thursday. Tobias is still laughing manically like yesterday, but yesterday, tears were far off and his pride was rampant. His sense of shame was obviously inactive and didn't affect his behaviour, as could be seen from the fact that he could hear me answer the phone several times and could hear who I was talking to, describing how he felt and behaved, without any protests from his side.

However, when, G, the assistant who Tobias hit on Tuesday phoned and wanted to hear how things were, Tobias, obviously upset, rushed up and snatched the receiver out of my hand and put it back on the hook.

Today he has been crying between his attacks of laughter, or been exaggeratedly loving towards Tore, and later, Mårten. But not towards me. He has been intimate towards me so many times earlier in this state, and we have discussed it so many times afterwards in his normal state, that it seems as if this boundary, the incest taboo, has been strengthened and is now functional between us, even during a psychosis. Now.

Today, Tobias is obviously ashamed about standing on the opened hatch of the dishwasher the other day. When he is going to put his breakfast dish into the dishwasher, Tore says: «Hold the hatch firmly, it falls down so heavily otherwise.»

Tobias then remembers what he had done, and can't stand the shame. He puts his hand on one of Tore's shoulders and leans his head upon the other; stays so for a long while, still, then sinks down heavily, falls to the floor and simulates an attack of epilepsy. Tobias has never ever simulated an attack! Tore watches how Tobias, without convulsions (he can't fake these), let his tongue hang out and makes gnashing sounds. When he «wakes up», Tore asks him if he's tired and wants to rest, to which he gratefully agrees.

Today, Tobias also folded his spectacles into four parts, and they broke. They are lying on the kitchen workbench and Tobias has persistently tried to show me that he can mend them. It seems to be important for Tobias to demonstrate this. To repair the guilt. It is also important to wash the dishes. Marten is his assistant during the day. Tobias demands that the dishwasher is to be started despite being only half full. This evening, while writing this, I understand that he needed to make sure that the dishwasher was still working, even though he had stood on the open hatch yesterday and that the hatch was a little bent.

We sit awhile before Mårten goes home and talk about feelings. I remark that yesterday, Tobias could identify an inner feeling of being unhappy. In front of Mårten, Tobias is very keen to deny this, though when I ask him for total honesty he admits it to a certain degree. I also say that I believe that he is ashamed about jumping upon the hatch of the dishwasher. He denies this, shrugging his shoulder, waving it away with a snort; he's not got a guilty conscience. I repeat my view, obstinately but kindly, that earlier today feelings of guilt were evident.

«Tobias, it was so unpleasant to be reminded of the dishwasher that you almost fainted!»

«Yes.»

I can see that he is aware of this.

It is time for Tobias to sleep for the night. I tell him the same tale as yesterday, a suitable, new, home-made variation of the Three Billy Goats Gruff who are going to cross a bridge under which a troll is living, and the troll, as usual, wants to eat up the goats one after another. The first, smallest, goat suggests that the troll waits until the next goat that is bigger and juicier, and in order to catch it one must be light and hungry. The same procedure with the next goat, the middle-sized goat. This evening, I mention that the middle-sized goat is perhaps Tobias, as he's the big brother of the smallest one. Tobias listens with closed eyes. This evening he has taken 8 mg Stesolid[12] but no Nozinan. It is the third day with Nozinan and I am beginning to see a pattern. With every psychosis that has needed medication, Tobias has needed Nozinan if the process has reached the point where Tobias is not responsive to discussion, lacks judgement and is driven by sexual or aggressive impulses. In the worst case, Tobias will need 3 - 4 x 25mg per day. Towards the end of the third day, such as today, we avoid further doses of Nozinan and just give him Stesolid at night. Then, he becomes more lucid, and is easier to calm than earlier. At this point he likes me to talk to him.

The tale of the Billy Goats Gruff gets a new twist. I take the opportunity of being therapeutic, and give him a chance to forgive, recover, and move on from shame to guilt and forgiveness.

---

12 Diazepam, sold as Valium in U.S.

I tell him the troll doesn't get thrown into the river by the largest goat, but is instead invited to cross the bridge and go to the meadow and live with the three Billy Goats Gruff. I tell him that they play together and the troll has difficulty believing that he is welcome. The troll asks if he really may be with them, since he has been so cruel. The biggest Goat Gruff tells the troll that he wasn't cruel at all, he did silly things and threatened people, but he was so lonely. One can be cruel when one is lonely and on the outside. Now, however, the troll will enjoy fellowship and become kind. Oh, is that really true? The troll needs assurance, and I repeat the goat's pledge that this is the truth. It looks as if Tobias is asleep by this point.

I repeat: «Yes, it's true, you are not really cruel. If you stay and play with us you will become kind, as you in fact really are. You were not cruel, only very miserable.»

I suddenly realise Tobias is wide-awake. He says:

«Miserable, me.»

«You were miserable?»

«Yes.»

«You are also loved, we love you and forgive you for all the silly things you've done.»

«All?»

«Yes.»

«All?»

«Yes.»

«The machine?»

«You mean the dishwasher?»

«Yes.»

«The dishwasher, too.»

I talk about the dishwasher. It is only a machine, and Tobias is a person with feelings. He has the most difficult situation in the family. It's a pity that the hatch was damaged, but it is much more a pity that Tobias lost control in that way – this hurts us, this is difficult. It is Tobias that suffers most. He relaxes and seems to be happy with the answer.

He wants to know how the dishwasher is now. I tell him in detail. I tell him that we can certainly buy a new hatch or new springs to the hatch. He says:

«Or me.»

«You want to buy them?»

«Yes.»

Fantastic. Here is a willingness to reparation, a mature and important ability of wanting to repay a debt. I don't put up any resistance. Should he go through with it, we can help him economically in some way so that he can afford this restoration for himself and for us.

I continue talking about how well he is loved and encourage him to sleep with this feeling of togetherness within the family, to sleep with the feeling of being liked and loved.

REFERENCE

Klein, M. (1988, 1993) *Kärlek, Skuld och Gottgörelse*. Sthlm: Natur& Kultur. In original: Love, Guilt and Reparation and Other Works 1921-1945. London: Hogarth Press. 1981.

INTEGRATION. FROM THE SCHIZO-PARANOID TO THE DEPRESSIVE POSITION

This chapter is suitable for the reader with an interest in psychological theories and the development of schools of thought, and how existential phenomena can be explained from a deep psychological perspective.

I have had invaluable support and help in bringing order to chaos from the explanatory models within Object relations theory, ORT. Tobias' bizarre behaviour when psychotic would have been totally unintelligible, repulsive, and frightening if I didn't have a reasonable theory to hold on to. It might even have increased the risk of Tobias being marginalized and beyond any of the psychological help he needed in order to manage his inner needs. If his inner world is viewed as an unintelligible, uninteresting chaos that can only be calmed by medicine and more medicine then he will remain totally alien for himself. As well as for us. Psychodynamic object relations theory, like the earlier psychoanalytic view of schizophrenia, is based upon theories that are firmly rooted in clinical experience.

Examples of experienced, knowledgeable, and qualified psychotherapists who have mapped and understood the deeper structure of psychosis from a clinical perspective are Harold Searles and Frieda Fromm Reichmann. Within the British tradition, we have Melanie Klein, Ronald Fairbairn, Harry Guntrip, Hanna Segal and the more independent Donald Winnicott, whose insights into the importance of aggression have given me good help in understanding psychosis and clients close to psychosis.

Tobias is a text book example of the process that is described in these theories. These theories are not fabrications made by fanatical psychologists that love to pluck fantastic constructions from out of thin air. No, the originators have taken their experiences of their patients as starting points, and with a genuine interest in the subconscious processes, they have tried to understand the seemingly inexplicable. The results have helped clinical therapists to stubbornly try to understand and thus cope with the subjective meanings behind mental illness.

Once the storm phase of Tobias' psychosis has passed on to a more anxious existence, somewhere between imagination and reality, an intensive communication starts. I must keep Tobias in a state of reality. I am trying to write this while Tobias watches TV, but I am interrupted time and again by Tobias who wants to translate the contents of the programme in terms of our relationship. Tobias is very involved in the question of Tore's good-will contra his ill-will. He is conscious of having been both aggressive and contemptuous. Now he's afraid of retaliation and he needs to be reassured time and again that Tore is not angry at him.

The process is as follows: There is total fragmentation during the storm phase. Owing to his terribly weak sense of self, the smallest indignity can give him cause to hit back, and, in lack of a verbal ability, it will be physical. He acts out a hate that he subsequently must flee from by avoiding the person who had been the object of his aggression. He sees his actions as being unforgivable and can't withstand the shame of being alienated, and beyond forgiveness. Therefore, his defence is to scorn and to isolate himself, invulnerable and unwanted. His whole body radiates coldness; his eyes are cold and grey, his skin, too. He is taking 25 mg Nozinan 3 x 4 times a day. He may even need 10 mg diazepam, so that he can sleep properly instead of wandering around or going out to find a neighbour to charm.

All his fantasies have one common theme: to relieve him of his anxiety, save him from his self-loathing and confirm him as a good person. Good is not enough, it has to be better than good. To counterweigh the powerful self-loathing demands a greater force than good, he must be shown to be something really special. The greater the feeling of shame and worthlessness, the greater is the defence. When the defence mechanism is, what Freud called, «reaction formation», it can, in extreme cases, lead to a conviction of being omnipotent and chosen to perform something exceptional. This time, however, it seems as if there are not so many fantasies remaining to escape to. It seems as if he has consumed so many fantasies during his earlier psychoses, and maybe his brain remembers that they gave very little relief. This time he has been demonstrating pure anger, an I-can-myself attitude, and a demonstrative independence. On day two, Wednesday, he received a certain amount of insight into the destructive consequences of anger; a ruined dishwasher hatch, a shocked and unhappy assistant, the burden of shame and the fear of his own destructivity.

At the moment, Tobias is watching a quiz-game on the TV. I can hear him answering. The answer is either A, B, C, or D. He shouts «One»! and shortly after he says «oh, good!» and gets up. I get up and go over to him and ask what was so good. He doesn't answer. «Did you know the answer?» I ask him. Tobias says yes.

«Was it good to get it right?»

«Yes.»

But then he makes a snorting gesture with his arm and says «Turn it off.» I'm surprised and remind him that he usually really likes this programme. So he sits back down and continues watching. This is not due to a lack of self-will, as I know he has a very strong will in important matters. So, in which way can I understand this little sequence? Yes, he had been really involved in the programme. However, in his weak state, he feels that being involved is a weakness. His self-sufficiency is threatened; he wants to be aloof so that he will not be affected if something is taken from him, for example the capacity to understand the questions. If there is anyone who has an implicit memory of having something taken from him, it is Tobias. Maybe he could not fool himself about not knowing the answer, about feeling inadequate.

Anyway, this is the form on day three of a typical Tobias psychosis.

The next fixation is with his eyesight and spectacles. After three days using neuroleptics and having a high level of anxiety, perhaps his eyesight is affected and his spectacles aren't really working properly? He sits a few minutes with them on, then he has to take them off, commenting about this aloud and asking me whether he really needs spectacles or not. Every time this happens I reply calmly and patiently that only he can answer the question of how well he can see. I encourage him to check whether he can see the TV best with or without them. I can't know, he knows. This satisfies him. For a few minutes.

He turns off the TV and walks quickly towards me with some intent in mind. He leans over me and puts his lips against my neck and I feel directly that he's going to give me a real tongue kiss. I back off and say that this is too close and intimate. He saves face directly and means that the kiss wasn't for me, but someone else. I wonder if he wants to kiss someone else?

«No.»

He points towards the bedroom.

«Tore?»

«Yes.»

«But you shouldn't be intimate with Tore, either.»

«No, not me. You!»

He, thus, solves an oedipal conflict by connecting Tore with me. Preferably right now, so that he doesn't have to feel that he has ruined anything.

«Tore is asleep and I will kiss him when we both want to.»

Tobias doesn't see this as an infringement; he is obviously in a regression to an oedipal position that coincides with the depressive position. At this stage, there is a need of connecting things, and a twosome must become a threesome, without jealousy ruining everything. Love wins over jealousy, bonding over disintegration, life over death, and love over hate, without the need for denial. Normal repression suffices perfectly. This raises self-respect.

Causes

We always try to understand. The incomprehensible, chaotic, and intractable phenomena that psychosis bears with it makes us search for causes, of course. Can we be better prepared next time? Can we forestall it in any way? Can we see early warning signs and pre-medicate so that the attack is milder?

Maybe.

I have met doctors who believe that the answer lies in constantly swallowing neuroleptics as a preventive care. This would mean that the brain would have to metabolise a medium or high dose constantly. Unthinkable! This is not a good alternative when I see what Nozinan does to Tobias when he needs it during the acute phase, making him giddy and unbalanced, giving him a rash, clouding his wakefulness so that he mumbles, and even giving him a body odour and breath that stinks. It seems like an ironic destiny that, only one week after I had written to Tobias' neurologists about how Tobias can perhaps look forward to milder attacks after beginning to use Lyrica[13], this strong attack should break out! I have also learnt that one of Tobias' assistants feels that Tobias' mood has been more uneven this last half-year. Lyrica has chemical

13 Pregabalin. At the time Tobias was prescribed Lyrica, confusion was not mentioned as a side effect. We realized that Tobias' states of confusion started and worsened while the drug was prescribed in higher and higher doses in accordance with the recommended treatment plan. After one year, we stopped the medication with Lyrica altogether and Tobias became free from confusion for several months, compared to weeks while on the medication. In 2012, confusion is reported to be a side effect in 1% of all users.

similarities to Nozinan and is classed as a neurolepticum. It is very popular at the moment. It is prescribed for pain, anxiety and epilepsy. Is it possible that Lyrica had a good effect in the beginning, a start effect that has now turned into a negative phase? Considering that no-one, absolutely no-one, can answer this question, then every patient must feel her way forward, carefully of course. We already know for certain that Stesolid, a diazepam, can be addictive. This can be seen from FASS (Swedish classification of pharmaceuticals) and I also happen to know that many doctors refuse to prescribe diazepam because of this. I remember the psychiatric care of the 80's when diazepam was the most common medicine for anxiety, and how, at the psychiatric hospital where I worked, there were so many cases of addiction, reduced effect, and increases in dosage. This is why we are very careful that Tobias only uses Stesolid sparingly, a few times a month at most.

Several factors can trigger off a psychosis and in those cases where a single insult to his self-esteem is the cause, dialogue and maybe a Stesolid before sleep can often prevent an attack. An alternative method is for me to sleep the night at Tobias' flat and be there to provide security and reality if a nightmare that he experiences as real wakes him during the night.

Trigger factors that we have identified are:
1) An event that reminds him of his inability to live in a way that he would have, had it not been for his injury.

Example a: Tobias has incidentally met an old school friend in town, who has said hello and taken for granted that Tobias is as he was earlier. His disability is not visible unless one knows about it and can recognize the slight half-side paralysis.

Example b: Tobias has either met or seen women that he desires and would have doubtless courted had it not been for his injury.

2) Tobias has had an epileptic fit at night and has fever the day after. If he ignores the fever and exposes himself to daily wear and tear, he is very vulnerable. He gets confused and shut in his own world, he would like to function, but can't. He doesn't know why, he just feels stupid and silly, more than usual, and this is a catastrophe that must be stopped! His rage comes like lightening. He behaves badly and feels even more foolish, which is so different from his self-image according to which he is calm, in control and worldly wise. Chaos.

We haven't been able to find any other trigger factors. There are roughly speaking two causes of the psychoses, more or less in combination with each other. A psychological cause, in the form of a weakened self-esteem, self-loathing and shame, as well as the neurological cause in the form of an epileptic fit in a brain that lacks words and that gets stuck in a state of stress if he has a fever.

I can thus draw two conclusions from experience. They consist of two roots down into the human soil of possibilities.

The importance of antipyretics when needed and the necessity of understanding the mystery of madness as the primitive language it, in fact, is. We, that is to say, the closest family and assistants, have raised our competence in order to prevent the destructive spiral of self-loathing.

REFERENCE

Fairbairn, W. Ronald D. (1994) *Psychoanalytical Studies of the personality.* London, New York: Routledge. In original: 1952. London: Tavistock Publications.

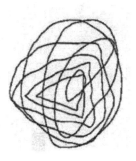

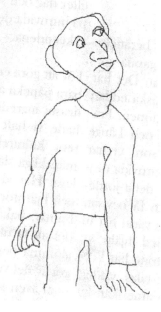

Drawing by Tobias

124

SWAP SOULS OR WEAR A MASK

A seizure during the night of the 24th of November 2008 well and truly knocks out Tobias' vocabulary. Tobias is both conscious of his deficiency and unconscious of the fact that it is only temporary due to the attack and his self-esteem sinks catastrophically. So catastrophically that he can't put up with himself. Logic, common sense, and the ability to reflect are disabled owing to the fatigue caused by the attack and an unwillingness to think, accept and understand, as well as an acute desire to deny reality. This is how I view the situation.

The symptoms show themselves on Wednesday morning when Tobias' lack of sense causes him to trespass the limits of proper affection towards his art teacher, who gets very embarrassed. Tobias' assistant, Jörgen, has to step in when Tobias can't be reasoned with and they both go home. Tobias becomes increasingly restless throughout the afternoon.

Tobias laughs madly and uncontrollably hysterically. But as Jörgen is experienced and has seen Tobias in this state earlier, he maintains an intensive dialogue with Tobias, does not lose contact with him, and doesn't let him flee into his own thoughts. He interprets and understands, with the result that Tobias starts crying. For some reason that we haven't managed to fathom, Tobias cannot cry for relief. He always cuts off his tears and flees reality. It is now that one can understand that his unrealistic behaviour and his lack of sense are torture even for Tobias himself. The whole afternoon Tobias repeats the phrase «brain as tiny as a pea». This is all he can think about.

Anders takes over from Jörgen. The thoughts, anxiety and restlessness continue. Tobias phones me at home and seemingly just the sound of my voice is enough to calm him, I can see no other solution just now than to try to strengthen his self-esteem over the phone. I talk to him about what he is good at; expressing himself in images. He answers with the occasional «yes», but is otherwise unusually quiet. After talking a little more I hear Anders ask «was the connection broken?», and Tobias says «yes» and puts the phone on the hook. Next day, Anders, and Tore, who has spent the night and Thursday morning with Tobias, say that Tobias has been acting as if he hasn't been able to understand what they were saying. He had either gone into an autistic bubble or his epileptic fit had temporarily shut down the parts of his brain that look after language comprehension.

Tobias spends Thursday with Tore, who now experiences a Tobias as he was at 4 years of age. He asks the meaning of and wants to understand every single word. He does it in the obstinate manner of a child. «What is brain» he might ask. If you explain that brain is a mass of nerve-cells he will then ask «Nerve-cells – what's that?» If you then explain that they are like wires that connect feelings to words, words to words, and thoughts, he will then ask «thoughts – what's that?» Yes, one's pedagogical ability is really put to the test.

The day passed well. Tobias was still feeling stupid, though, as could be seen when he looked at Tore and said, «You are clever, I am not clever».

Tobias, Tore, and Mårten set off to fetch Mårten's son, Wille, from preschool. During the car-ride Tobias starts clicking his fingers to the beat of the music on the car-radio. When the music is turned off he can't stop clicking. Then, he starts behaving in a manner one sometimes sees in people with schizophrenia: He seems to think intensively, then looks up and calls out slowly and in a way that demands attention: «Aaaaaaaah! That's it, ahaaa … mm, now I understand!» Then he gets hold of Tore and says «Thanks!!! You're gooood!!! … » Replay. The same thing over and over again. Since he continues acting in this way on the boat out to the island, Tore decides not to provoke him by intervening and waits until they arrive home and then he gives Tobias some simple, mundane household duties such as laying the table. He also gives him a neuroleptic pill and encourages him to «Come out to me!» while giving him lots of praise for every simple daily activity he performs.

When I come home in the evening we continue in this way, helping each other to keep Tobias within the realms of reality.

Friday: Not much of what I had planned gets done. Tore and I take turns; whoever is using the computer is free from Tobias. Tobias can't stand himself. How else can one interpret his wanting to be someone else? For some reason we mention the concept «soul». Tobias looks at me and makes a loop motion with his hand, and says:

«You and me, change.»

«Do you mean changing souls with me?»

Yes, that's what he wants. It takes numerous discussions to convince Tobias that it is neither possible, nor desirable.

«Would you really like to sit all day with my clients at work? Do you really not want to be able to paint anymore?»

«No ... no.»

Later that evening, Tobias' low self-esteem shows itself again when he asks:

«I have a mask?»

One can wonder what on earth he is talking about, and dismiss this crazy attempt at conversation. However, I decide to be patient and try to understand. I ask myself why anyone would want to wear a mask. Well, yes, in order to hide away. The same theme again. If one can't exchange identities with someone more fortunate then maybe one can get a new identity by wearing a mask. Tore and I interpret; we understand the need and add that we want him just as he is. He thankfully accepts this but then spends the rest of the evening assuring us repetitively that he doesn't need a mask.

I tell him about when he was born, how he was when very young, I tell him memories and try to get him to realise that he is Tobias and he has his past. He understands.

«You, Tobias, are all your experiences, everything you have experienced is you.»

Tobias is happy with this explanation.

«Your accident is also a part of your experience.»

«Yes, true, true.»

Tobias becomes thoughtful.

He obviously wants us to keep telling him that he is fine as he is. But, by half past eleven in the evening with everyone in bed for the night, Tobias gets up for the third to time to ask the same question and I emphasise that it is time for this to stop:

«It's time for you to stay in bed and stop bothering us with questions. We all need to sleep!!!»

Tobias understands, and sleeps. He had taken 2 mg diazepam an hour earlier, which maybe made it easier for him to fall asleep. Maybe, but if he had been more manic, a small dose would have had no effect. So, I'm happy that he listened to my directive.

The next morning is Saturday. It is my birthday.

Tore tells Tobias that I am sitting writing about how Tobias is today. He asks:

«Today?»

Tore tries to explain the concept «today» as compared to «yesterday» and «tomorrow». Tobias understands.

«Today, is Susanna's birthday. Not yesterday or tomorrow, but today is her birthday. Do you know what a birthday is?»

«No.»

«To have a birthday is to celebrate the day one was born, a long time ago. Do you understand?»

«No.»

«Ok, then you'll have to wonder what to have a birthday means.»

«What!!! Wonder??»

«I am talking to you and it doesn't seem as if you understand a single word, as if you can't understand anything I say.»

«No.»

«Do you understand what I'm saying?» Tore asks.

«No.»

He is totally lost, now.

I think I understand even though I can only guess. The words take on a new life and sound strange. The unconscious, implicit memory on the other hand, a kind of implicit autonomous authority, intuitively understands the contents of what is being said. However, as Tobias thinks that he must consciously understand the meaning of every word, the situation becomes hopeless at the present moment. I explain this:

«You understand intuitively, even if you don't understand every word.»

«What's intuitively?»

«It's a feeling, you understand what we mean.»

«What!»

Tobias points at his injury.

«I'm confused now.»

«There are a lot of words in your head that are confusing you?»

«Yes.»

«What can one do about that?» I ask.

Tobias answers:

«Lots.»

«Yes, maybe one can do lots of things, like rest, for instance.»

«Yes.»

Tobias goes and lies down to rest a while. He gets up after two minutes, absorbed by the word «note» that has seemingly come from nowhere. We spend the next twenty minutes drawing notes, we draw the whole scale and sing the scale. I help him to understand what notes are, and he understands. When he repeats the word «note» and looks worried, I explain that even I will lose my feeling for a word if I repeat it time and time again.

Aren't there many of us who recognize this phenomenon? I experienced it sometimes as a child, even as a teenager. I could go around and think about a word, and every time I tasted the word, the word became more and more strange. As if I had never heard it before.

It's probably a good thing that I'm a little crazy too.

Adult?

It's still Saturday and my birthday. Tobias is still repeating the word «note», and if we had a little less fortitude and were a little more uneasy, we would have drugged him to escape all this annoying repetitiveness.

But, our fortitude is rewarded. Tobias accompanies me to the boat to meet Mårten and our grandson, Wille, who have come to celebrate my birthday. My daughter-in-law, Pia, and their little youngest child are staying at home in the hope that, with a little luck, she can have a good night's rest. Wille is teething, is bothered by jealousy and has just started pre-school so the nights are not especially peaceful. While we walk towards the boat I chat about the weather. It is stormy.

Tobias repeats: «Storm. Storm … Storm … Storm.»

He sounds calm. I can hear no desperation in his voice. I get an association. It's like when I learned Spanish in school and I repeated words time and again in different contexts, when walking, or riding on a tram, for instance. I did it to make the word stick in my mind. This is perhaps just what Tobias is doing. It seems to be conscious and disciplined, not crazy and obsessive like earlier today. After a while Tobias says:

«Storm … the wind is whining».

This association is perfectly correct! The words don´t just come by themselves in some kind of ad hoc chemical manner within the brain. It promises well!

Only a week ago, Tobias came in contact with a speech therapist. Habilitating services are usually only provided to people with congenital disabilities, not individuals that have suffered brain damage as an adult. However, rehabilitation must end somewhere, mustn´t it? I raise this question, as the answer is not so apparent. A really demanding family member can almost certainly get rehabilitating services all the way up to the point when the client reaches the age of pension, but I haven't managed to find a rehabilitation service that has been worth applying for at this stage, so long after the accident. We had fortune on our side. Thanks to the local authority´s ambition to avoid costs for Tobias' schooling by recommending a special school and the special school for adults with learning disabilities' willingness to take on Tobias, which they didn't really need to do, Tobias came automatically in contact with a speech therapist, a physiotherapist and a psychologist. At this time, they are considering what they can do for Tobias. I have spoken to the speech therapist and she understands that Tobias has a very severe global aphasia, that he demands respect for his own integrity and that he needs everyone who wants to help him to evoke his unique personal motivation.

I experience the meaning of high motivation today. I am standing in front of the bathroom mirror trying to straighten my hair with straightening irons. Tobias is observing me. I say:

«I'm straightening my hair.»

Tobias repeats:

«Straight … straight … straight … (silence) … not wavy!»

A totally correct association. He wants to learn, he wants to find words, and he wants to live!

Tobias and assistant Anders

WORDS AND APPEALS. KNOWING THAT ONE DOES NOT KNOW

One step back ... and then two forward, is what I usually say, encouragingly, to those of my patients who have had a set-back in their development and healing. Sometimes I have heard the following answer: «No, two steps backwards and just possibly one step forward.» Just one step.

This is exactly how I experience Tobias when, towards the end of November 2007, he suffers yet another attack of confusion and a flight from reality. It was only recently he had his latest psychosis, just a few weeks ago. That time it all started with Tobias being extremely affectionate towards his art teacher. As I wrote above, Tobias was so affectionate that his art teacher became embarrassed. His assistant was quick to head this off, but Tobias couldn't manage to concentrate on the task of the day and continued to show his teacher ex-aggerated affection and gratitude. His assistant could see no other solution than to go home with Tobias earlier than usual. I have described what happened after this in the previous chapter. «A brain as small as a pea» is what Tobias said. The next few days revolved around the subject of how small his brain is, to be transformed into unrealistic attempts at sol-ving the problem by, for instance, swapping souls with me. A deeper talk concerning what this would involve and what my workday is like, made Tobias realize how unrealistic an exchange of souls would be. That same evening, Tobias came upon the idea of a mask, like a theatrical mask, as a solution. Tobias was able to drop this idea, too, as soon as Tore mana-ged to convince Tobias that a mask is only surface, and that he would be the same under the mask, and that this Tobias is good as he is. However, he needed help. During the whole evening, Tobias demanded attention and wanted us to see and agree that «Now – no mask». We had to agree, tell him that he understands now, and that he is good enough as he is. During the following day, Tobias continued to be occupied with the same phenomenon, but obviously more conscious of the fact that it had to do with the magnitude of his brain damage and the consequent devaluation of his self-esteem.

We were forced to talk in this way for several days. Tore and I took turns to talk with Tobias about his situation and his great need of assistance. He was amazed and moved by the severity of his own aphasia.

We are on the express bus going to Saltholmen. On this kind of bus, everyone gets on through the door at the front, so that the driver can see that one has paid. Tobias has a pre-paid month-ticket in the form of a pass so he has nothing to stamp on the ticket machine. He simply walks onto the bus and finds a seat. When Tobias has almost got to a free seat and lots of people are getting onto the bus, the driver calls out: «You there, you haven't paid!» I call back to the driver that Tobias has a pre-paid ticket. Some of the passengers sitting at the front confirm this, adding that they know Tobias. I hear the driver mutter something that sounds official, as if he needs proof that he is doing his job properly. I ask Tobias to get out his ticket from his wallet. This takes a while since he can't remember what it is he is supposed to find there. He finds his identity card and I suggest to him that it is perhaps a good idea to show it to the driver, too. I find his ticket for him and Tobias goes forward with both documents in his left hand, which he also has to use to hold on as the bus is swerving quite strongly through the curves. At the next bus-stop, Tobias shows the ticket and the identity card. He then returns to his seat. Tobias says to me:

«Chaotic and difficult!»

After I asked him a few questions, I begin to understand that he thinks the driver could have let things be and not been so fussy. I tell him that some people cheat, and don't pay, and that the driver can't be certain that Tobias is honest. You can't see that by just looking. I ask Tobias how he thinks it would have been if he had travelled alone and been asked to show his ticket. He doesn't know, and he wouldn't have remembered that he has a pre-paid month-ticket in his wallet. I asked him if there would have been a risk that he had then paid a one-way ticket. Yes, Tobias imagines that he would have done so. That would have cost him 30 crowns. A lot of money for someone retired and with a low income.

So there is yet another insight for Tobias to digest, the fact that he is dependent upon assistants in order to travel on public transport. Tobias is quiet and thoughtful. He looks at me and asks «three years?» He means that it will take three years to train his memory up to the point where he can remember his monthly ticket himself if he should be asked for it by the ticket inspectors. Actually, I know that he can remember his ticket when the inspectors behave in their normal manner –suddenly getting up, leaning over one's shoulder, and demanding in one's ear «TICKET CONTROL». Tobias has experienced this a few times and on a good day he will remember what it is they want to see. However, it is not the same routine when a bus driver asks to see his ticket and asks in a different manner. This is a new event for Tobias and he doesn't understand what it means.

Thus, Tobias understands that he doesn't understand.

When we speak and act we usually make use of our implicit memory. Within this memory system is everything we do automatically, and don't need to make decisions about, actively choose or actively understand. We do things by pure routine. We use our implicit memory very much when we communicate with each other. When you read these lines, you understand the meaning of what I have written without needing to check your understanding of every single word in the sentences. This is a function that presumes that you know the language and that you have stored the words by having repeated them for many years while learning to read English.

Tobias is behaving like a two year-old who repeats words, asks what the words mean, savours them over a longer period of time and repeats them aloud to himself. This is also the way we learn a foreign language. It is not enough just to listen, guess and have a vague idea about the meaning of sentences, we must actively pronounce the words, create sentences and repeat, repeat. This is what Tobias is doing with Swedish right now. The only reason for doing this is that he feels that he must repeat the words if they are to become his own tools.

He realizes that he has the language of a two year-old, is as emotionally developed as a 15 year-old and is a 23 year-old in other ways. He cannot explain but I imagine that he has a mature well developed grip on questions such as culture and the arts, social relationships and existential matters. He lacks words in these areas of course, so one has to know Tobias quite well to realize his maturity in these matters.

These powerful insights have led to some rather overwhelming conclusions. Tobias realizes that he pretends to know more than he really does. He has given priority to seemliness, casual niceness, and showing off a good self-confidence, at the cost of a deeper understanding. While taking part in daily activity group tasks, it is not uncommon that he pretends he understands when he doesn't. In conversation he lets people believe that he doesn't know the answer when in fact it is the question he doesn't understand. Just try reading the previous sentence and re-living this yourself. So frustrating!

Now it is time to stop running away from reality, says Tobias. He lives up to it, too, at least during the week after he made this giant leap forward towards new insights. It has also led to consequences that are not so easily realized. Let me explain.

Tobias has a young, pleasant assistant. She is Tobias' type of woman, as everyone already knows. A few weeks ago, while on the boat, a neighbour asked how Tobias is getting on nowadays and how many assistants he has. We listed them all and when the only female assistant was mentioned, the neighbour asked, with a glint in his eye, if she was good looking. Tobias wasn't slow to smile and agree that she was.

If Tobias had not had his injury and been perfectly healthy, and had told a male friend that he had employed a new secretary, how would the question «is she good looking?» have been received?

Tobias understands the difference. He is treated as if it is sweet that he has got an attractive assistant, even though he has the same longing for a real affair of the heart as anyone else. This gets forgotten when one asks him «is she good-looking?» It is purely out of respect for the askers' naivety that he refrains from showing his frustration.

Drawing made by Tobias

UNDERSTANDING

It is June again, and Tobias is staying with us for a few days around Midsummer. It's lovely weather.

We are eating breakfast. A little yoghurt fastens in the corner of Tobias mouth. This is not an everyday occurrence since he is not very lame in his face. This is why we haven't got used to seeing bits of food in the weaker corner of the mouth, which I know many people live with every meal, every day, without being bothered by it.

However, every family and every group of assistants have expectations that are slightly higher than the level at which the disabled individual functions. To encourage awareness about the best possible table manners and a food-free face, is perhaps an instinctive concern in much the same way that parents to small children are half a step ahead of their children's development as regards responses and expectations.

«You've got some food in the corner of your mouth.»

Tobias feels round his mouth with his finger. He finds the bit of food but doesn't know what to do with it.

To be perfectly honest, this is frustrating for me as well. It's not easy to get used to the fact that one's adult son can't either go and fetch a napkin or just like a child, lick his finger.

«Lick your finger.» I say.

This is how relatives behave sometimes.

We have eaten breakfast and Tobias has showered. I give him a hug. His hair doesn't smell so nice. He smells dirty. So I ask him to get back under the shower and listen carefully to my instructions.

«Wet all your hair under the shower.»

It's important that he understands every single word.

Tobias gets back under the shower and turns on the water. Instinctively, he grabs the soap and starts washing his belly.

When he starts in this way, I know that I will have to inspect the whole showering process as the hair shampooing may be forgotten otherwise.

As stubborn as a mule, I would like to imprint a routine that starts with hair shampooing! I would also like to break the habit he has, when finally finding the shampoo bottle, of pouring a quarter of its contents over his head under running water and letting it all get rinsed directly away.

He is standing under the shower with his head forward, getting his neck wet.

«All your hair. Wet all your hair,» I say.

I want to imprint a good routine into his procedure memory and this is a challenge.

I have to ask Tobias again to lean his head backwards.

«Lean your head so that the side gets wet, too … And the other side.»

I then give him a little shampoo to use, but he just wipes it backwards and forwards over the top of his head.

«The side as well, massage it in. On the right side, too.»

Is he ever going to become conscious of the existence of his right side?

I leave him there and go out. Tobias comes out from the bathroom dressed in my dressing gown. I only comment on this detail by saying: «Aha, you're using my dressing gown are you?»

Knowing Tobias as I do, and using my intuition, I imagine that he looked for his blue dressing gown in a routine manner, but when he couldn't see it he took the nearest one to hand, mine.

I try not to care about details like these, but deep inside I feel a frustration about his inability to deal with problems at a deeper level than this. If Tobias had this ability, then his taking the easy way out and using my dressing gown instead of searching for his own would irritate me in the way a teenager is irritating when acting like this. Deciding what is worth correcting and what can be tolerated is a constant exercise in judgement and self-discipline.

Tobias' pants are left lying by the wash-basin when he leaves the bathroom.

«You can put them into our washing basket,» I tell Tobias.

Tobias picks up the pants and wanders aimlessly around. He can't remember last summer's routine.

«In our room,» I say.

Tobias goes towards his own room.

«Our! Our means Susanna's and Tore's.»

Tobias goes to our room and looks around. I show him the basket and now he recognizes it.

I dedicate this chapter to the sad fact that Tobias' inabilities frustrate us in the family. Is it just as frustrating for Tobias himself? Probably not, as he would then almost certainly be unhappy most of the time and luckily enough he isn't. But when he is frustrated it is so unbearably strong that it causes him to flee to another world.

As a parent, one is exposed to abnormal frustrations that one is not equipped to deal with. Caring for disabled is not a part of our genetic constitution. However, I believe we have an inborn tendency to encourage and even expect growth, development, and eventually some form of independence for our offspring. When my adult son has a messy finger after eating and can neither go and fetch a napkin nor just lick it clean, then he is neither child nor adult. I said «Lick your finger.» Why did I say that?

I feel that I wanted a kind of consistency in his behaviour. I wanted to find a way to be open minded and to accept his level, just then. I was tired of assisting, in the sense of tactfully encourage the adequate use of a napkin.

If my professional, helping discretion had its way, then I would have made a minimal, hardly noticeable measure to go and get napkins and then sublimely, hardly noticeably brought his attention to their existence. Most probably, Tobias would have taken a napkin, wiped his mouth and not thought about the matter anymore.

I just did not want to be an assistant right now. I just wanted him to be left in peace at his actual level. Probably a level where it is okay to lick one's finger or a level where an adult goes and fetches him a napkin.

However, perhaps he is at both these levels at the same time. He stops the impulse to lick his finger because an adult part or rather a parent part of him censors this behaviour. But he can't find an alternative, not because of immaturity but because of his disability that means that his brain can't find the word for napkin, and maybe not even the idea, the inner image of a napkin. In that case he needs help, of course.

«Has Tobias' understanding declined?» asks Tore.

We talk about this. I don't believe it has. I believe he has stopped pretending to understand when in fact he doesn't. This is progress. It will now be more obvious just how much he does understand. This will make it easier to find the right level when talking to him and instructing him.

We too, have developed. We now dare to face up to tragic insights. In one month it will have been eleven years. We still have a very, very disabled son. It feels forlorn, since most people only want to see progress and they exaggerate the progress so that everyone can be happy. It must be terrible for friends and neighbours to hear about our defeats and disappointments. I can almost feel how they think: «Leave us in peace from this strange, unthinkable, terrible fate. Leave us to enjoy our budding, highly-functional children in peace! Don't make us try to understand, we don't want to.»

Tore and I have to, we have no choice, and we don't want to burden anyone else, we really don't. It's just that I'm so involved in thoughts and feelings sometimes that if someone asks a routine question about how things are, I answer honestly.

And how things are; it depends always, always, on Tobias' current state.

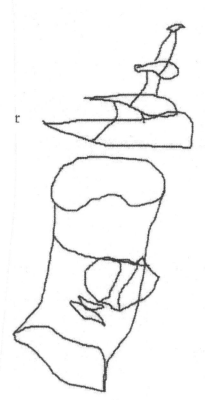

Drawing by Tobias

142

TALKING WITH GLOBAL APHASIA

Tobias doesn't remember the names of the people he meets during the day. If he does remember who he has met and what he has done, which is not self-evident, he very rarely takes the initiative to talk about it. However, if I ask him about his day, where he has been and who he has met, he will try to remember and sometimes he will recall some situations from the last few days. Maybe from the day in question, maybe from the day before. Really, it doesn't matter that much, as the important thing is that he does remember parts of his day and I must give up any wishes I might have that Tobias has a normal memory.

In order to tell something he will use expressions such as the following:

«Tall person», «over» while making a curve with his hand. One must use one's imagination. Did Tobias walk over the hill in his neighbourhood in order to come to the place where the meeting took place?

It is difficult for him to tell about his daily activities. However, to talk of here and now, and how he experiences the present moment is much easier.

An example:

I am talking to Tobias and Tore about hypnosis and its usefulness. Tobias almost never shows any interest in anything that he cannot relate to himself and his own experiences. He wants me to explain the principles of hypnosis so that he can understand. I give some examples and Tobias wants to tell me that he understands the word.

He wants us to get up from the dining-table. He does this by gesticulating with his hand and saying «come». He takes us into the bathroom and first points to the WC and then at the space above the bath-tub, while making circles with his finger in the air. You, the reader, either cannot make sense of how Tobias connects this with hypnosis, or maybe you have a fantastic ability to associate and are on the right track.

Since he remembers how the morning was, when I wasn't at home, Tore asks if this is about this morning when Tobias sat a very long time on the toilet. Did he go into a state of hypnosis then? Yes, he did.

And the bath?

Tobias shows with his fingers; he shows oblong figures in the air with a finger.

«Did you see figures there?»

«Yes.»

«What kind of figures?»

He can't find the words. Now, one has to just trust intuition. My intuition tells me that this is about all he can tell us.

I look into the air there and my imagination gives me the idea that Tobias has landed in a spontaneous state of trance or hallucination. I ask if he has seen angels there and he says «yes!», surprised that I guessed correctly.

The sceptical reader might imagine that he would have agreed with anything I had guessed as he hadn't really known what it was he had seen. However, I know Tobias, and he would not have agreed with just anything, unless we had been with other people. Just now we are alone. Despite his aphasia, he has a very good ability to distinguish between «right answer», «maybe», «sort of», and «wrong». In his vocabulary this is: «exact», «don't know», «almost!» and «not!»

Sometimes, however, details or truth are not so important. When Tobias wants to be the centre of focus he can make use of whatever means he wants. After a walk on Brännö, he came home and said:

«Fell down on the hill.»

I felt like questioning this. I asked him how he fell down, where he hurt himself, and whether he in fact did fall down.

«No, I didn't.»

He was joking. He hadn't fallen down at all. He just wanted a bit of attention. Just like when he was ten years-old, and a master of trickery. He was very convincing. This trait has returned, now.

Maybe Tobias just tried to tell me that he was proud of not having fallen down on that very steep hill.

Aphasia is difficult to cope with. Assistants and relatives mustn't give up trying to communicate. The afflicted mustn't be left misunderstood, more than necessary.

Guidance and counselling are needed. Psychological support is needed.

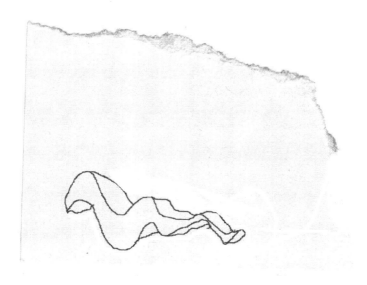

Drawing by Tobias

EVERYDAY HEROES

Everything is possible in the world of the psychotic. Omnipotent thoughts can change the world. How does it work? I learn all the time and I will never learn everything.

It is Easter 2008, and Easter has been a critical time for Tobias since the accident as far as I can remember. Tobias has been free from attacks for three weeks now, and unusually present and attentive. Clear and awake, it is wonderful!

Then one late afternoon, my mobile telephone rings while I am on the way to the tram. Mårten asks where I am and I tell him I am on the way to the 20.20 boat.

«Would you like to come and visit me and Tobias?» asks Mårten cheerily.

I understand from his tone of voice that he doesn't wants to risk upsetting Tobias with audible information telling me that the situation is precarious. However, the non-verbal information gets through to me and I say:

«Of course, I'll come right over.»

Tobias opens the door laughing. He is rather over-excited and his eyes are cool, but not unpleasantly cold as they can be sometimes. We go into the kitchen where Mårten has been preparing dinner. Tobias says:

«Zenit.»

Mårten explains that Tobias has wanted to go and take a coffee at the Café Zenit today.

«He's been totally fixated with Zenith, but I have persuaded him to make coffee here at home. Now we are going to cook some salmon. Would you like some, too?»

«Yes, please, I was just on the way home to have dinner, so I am hungry.»

While Mårten prepares the dinner I sit in the living room with Tobias. He agrees that he is a little over-active in his head. I now decide to give him a Nozinan as my experience tells me that he is going to get more manic. I also know by experience that he will get increasingly negative towards medication the more manic he becomes, so I have to be smart. I mustn't get into power struggles with a manic Tobias as I would never win. Therefore, I ask:

«I wonder which pill is most suitable for you right now. A Stesolid or a Nozinan? Stesolid is relaxing; you will be relaxed in your muscles. Nozinan takes away weird thoughts. Which would you choose right now?»

«Again!»

I describe the pill's functions once again and Tobias says:

«Weird thoughts.»

«You want to take away the weird thoughts. Take a Nozinan then.»

We are still sitting on the sofa when Tobias suddenly says «Zenit», whereby I remind him that we are going to eat soon. Tobias sits quietly for a short while. Suddenly, he has had enough of being reasonable. He goes and fetches his shoes and puts them on with a determined look in his eyes. I can't reach him with words and definitely not physically. And he's quick. Like a flash he is out of the flat and I hurry to put on my outer clothes, get his coat and scarf and catch up with him. I get to him seconds before he gets to Zenit's entrance. Through the plate-glass windows I can see a young man cleaning the floor, a woman cleaning the kitchen, and another man sitting on a chair waiting for his friend in the kitchen to finish today's work. I tell Tobias that Zenit is closed for the day, as can be seen by reading the notice with opening times that I point out. Very determinedly and a little aggressively, Tobias grabs the door handle and – it is not locked yet! Perhaps a bad luck, or good luck, ´cause a locked door might lead to banging on it and in the worst case some broken glass? I don't know how far he might take things.

Tobias walks firmly all the way up to the counter. I follow after him like a foolish guardian, telling him it's closed, and asking for confirmation from the young man on the chair. He confirms that it is closed. He can see that Tobias doesn't want to take «no» for an answer and tells him that they closed at eight o'clock and that he is not a customer but a friend waiting.

Tobias remains stubbornly by the counter. He leans over and calls into the kitchen:

«Hallo!»

I repeat that it is 20.25 and that they have closed for the day and that the staff has to go home, they're not getting paid and they have finished their shift. I think I have hit upon a respectful strategy so I tell Tobias I understand that he hadn't realized that it was already eight o'clock. I get no response other than a grimace that says he is ready for a power struggle. I feel anger and don't know whether it is mine or his. He makes me powerless and my total lack of influence makes me scared and angry. Yet, there is something in his expression that can be construed as – not anger, no, but something between hate, contempt and arrogance. So, I continue, telling him calmly that he is behaving badly, that one cannot force the café to accept him like this, that they have a right to call the police and in that case I would prefer an ambulance to hospital and a calming injection. His expression shows me that he would prefer that solution rather than leave by his own free will.

The man sweeping the floor intervenes by offering Tobias a bun. No, he is psychologically sounder than that, he doesn't discriminate Tobias, he invites us both.

«You're welcome to have a bun each if you want, before I clear up the counter.»

I look at Tobias and wonder what he makes of this offer.

«Ok,» he says and takes a bun. I take one, too, even though we are on the way home to have our salmon as soon as possible.

Tobias sits down at the newly-cleaned table and I suggest we eat our buns as we walk home. However, it is the role of «sitting in a café» that Tobias has been longing for all day. So, we sit there a while. When we finally walk homewards, Mårten comes to meet us as he has become worried and has wondered if I am in need of physical assistance. It has happened before, and violence is something we have come to expect. But I always think that it's not going to go that far this time.

At home, Mårten serves up the salmon. Tobias has difficulty in deciding: first he wants the plate with the smallest portion, then he wants the one with the most. I ask him now if he wants one or two pills of Nozinan. He says that one is enough, and luckily he has already forgotten the one he took before our little outing. He is asleep by 21.00, and I lie down on the sofa. My level of epinephrine is high and my brain is very awake and vigilant. Every time I am about to fall asleep, I am awoken by the shaking of my left foot the way Tobias' foot behaves, in his epileptic cramps. This goes on for a couple of hours and I get to wondering how much of Tobias' brain activity has been caught and imitated by my brain's mirror neurons.

I awake nervous as to who my son, Tobias, is going to be to-day. What will I meet, what must I cope with?

Tobias showers, which, as I can see, means standing under the running water. So I instruct him, but it is pointless to talk about shampoo or soap as he doesn't react to my instructions. I have to show him clearly and hold the shampoo as well as showing him how to use it.

I make breakfast, as Tobias can't manage anything practical today. Tobias sits at table with his breakfast in front of him, but forgets to eat if not reminded. When he finally starts he continues, which is a comfort. We have seen worse.

I tell Tobias about yesterday and what had happened at Zenit. He agrees that it is craziness.

He sleeps for a while again. When he awakens I want to see whether he can manage meeting other people. Whether he can manage all the impressions out on the street. It is always a greater risk here in town than on Brännö, as people know Tobias there and there is tolerance about his having a bad day. I suggest that we go to the flower shop to buy a potted plant for his kitchen. Tobias agrees, he is easy-going and flexible, while still understanding that he can make errors of judgement. Lovely!

After buying a pot plant that he let me choose, and which I paid for myself, naturally, (how interested has Tobias ever been in pot plants?), I suggested a visit to Zenit. By tone of voice and expression, Tobias shows how nicely surprised, grateful and even amazed he is by this suggestion and he readily agrees.

He is absolutely not over the crisis as can be seen from small signs such as not standing in the queue but beside it, picking up a spoon from the floor that a child has dropped and giving it back to the child, as well as being ready to leave after only drinking half his coffee. On the way home, I suggest walking through the small, sunny park. Tobias indicates that he wants to walk the usual route along the pavement, now in shadow. When he sees my determination and that I let him go his own way, he comes to meet me half way. There has been no need for Nozinan today, which is promising. Tore and Mårten turn up at Tobias' flat in order to make their way to Saltholmen and the boat to Brännö. Tore has taken Thursday off so as to be with Tobias. I set off to a scheduled meeting at work. It's been a long day.

To summarize the message in this chapter, it would be that it is aimed at people who work in cafés, shops etcetera. Mentally or cognitively disabled people, who have the privilege of living within the community with the help of assistants and escorts, assisted living or family carers, go to cafés. They shop in shops and go to the hairdresser. If you, who have no specific training in psychology and special education, can meet the desperation of a mentally disabled person with respect, calm and a flexible compromise between normal routines and a compliant exception from the standard routine, you can actually prevent someone having to make a degrading intervention with the use of a straitjacket, or a fast-acting injection and an ambulance. This may sound drastic but this is what remains when faced with a person who refuses to accept civil boundaries. By meeting Tobias' desperate need of being confirmed as a regular guest, the man in the café saved Tobias' fragile self-esteem from violation, the consequences of which are hard to imagine. Most likely a quick transport to the psychiatric emergency clinic would have been a probable though sad alternative. The man working in the café, one of these everyday heroes, probably saved thousands of Swedish crowns for Swedish health care.

They also saved Tobias from being degraded and thrown out of the café. Thank God for clever people and everyday heroes.

Drawing by Tobias

LOVE AND SEX

Three Mondays in a row, Tobias has been very tired, confused and sleepy. In this kind of situation, the assistants need to put their heads together and think – is there a pattern here?

We reached a hypothesis. On Sundays, Tobias watches the detective series, «Beck», on a commercial TV channel. Afterwards, this channel has been left on and Tobias has continued to watch when the assistant has gone home at around 22.00.

The same evening, pornographic films are also shown. Sexual needs are awakened. We think that this could be an explanation.

This Monday, Tobias had left his flat early in the morning, before his assistant turned up. He had gone to Café Zenit. He is a regular there and feels at home. He has also had his eye on girls there. Of course, the café is closed this early in the morning, so Mårten found him outside and they went home again. Mårten had guessed correctly – if Tobias isn't at home when someone comes, then he will have gone looking for somewhere that represents his own independent life, somewhere he can go whenever he wants to. Tobias is a person in his own right at Zenit. This is confirmed by the other regulars, such as Janne, an older artist, who always speaks to Tobias directly, and not via his assistants.

When they get home and he takes a shower, Tobias finds it impossible to follow Mårten's suggestion on how to wash his hair. Mårten gives up after four attempts. Mårten thinks that Tobias is trying to satisfy his sexual needs, though he doesn't want to question him on this private subject. Besides, it doesn't really matter whether he washes his hair or not, he will do that anyway on Sunday when he is at our house. Tobias has very thick hair that stays clean enough for several days. Just today, hygiene isn't top priority.

Mårten wants to try and keep to routines, though, and physical training is on the agenda on Mondays. Concentrating upon one's body while training physically doesn't only help physically, muddled thoughts can be calmed as well.

When Mårten suggests that he should pack his gym-bag, he just puts his shoes on. He seems unable to listen or follow instructions. We know by now that this is about concentration and attention. When these are muddled it is often because something else is «in the way». Tobias is caught up in something. He hears that he is getting instructions and makes a guess at some routine or habit that may happen to be correct. But he doesn't catch the meaning of the instruction; he can't manage to interpret the words and translate them into action.

Anyway, the day passes by without incident, but the gym-training is heavy and he gets a small nose-bleed. Something is sucking Tobias' energy, but what?

We think about this and discuss it together. How can we help Tobias?

I phone Tobias in the evening to hear how he is. It's not too good. I ask him if he possibly kept himself awake watching TV 1000 and the pornographic films that can be seen there. He answers «no». But this «no» sounds a little dutiful, rather as if «no» is how he feels he ought to answer.

After telling him that it is quite normal that someone single may be in need of sexual stimulation via a film, he agrees that this is what happened. He's been watching a pornographic film on TV. After speaking to Tobias, I have a word with the assistant who will continue this talk with Tobias. The assistant can see that the subject embarrasses Tobias. However, Tobias clearly supports the idea of buying a softcore film. The reason the assistant has suggested softcore is our hypothesis that Tobias has been watching pornography on the TV. The assistants have had time to discuss the matter and they know that the pornography on TV is «hard-core». We guess that this has turned Tobias off and that he couldn't get any relief this way, and instead lay awake, unsatisfied and sleepless. This suggestion leads to them going over to the video store. One might imagine that it is an impulse purchase to buy so many films, but we who have listened to Tobias' views are of the same opinion; his sexual morality is disturbed by crude porn.

On Tuesday, Tobias wakes in good form and the day passes nicely. After lunch, Tobias has another nose-bleed to which he reacts by sobbing his heart out. Tears are replaced by laughter. This shifting between tears and laughter is a typical sign that Tobias is entering a psychotic manic state, and the assistant phones to Mårten for guidance. Mårten phones to Tore who then takes Tobias home to us on Brännö. A Nozinan at 17.00 calms him down and Tobias then sleeps, with just a few visits to the toilet, from 19.00 until 09.00 the following day. This is perhaps his first really good sleep for two days as we don't know how he sleeps when he is alone.

We take a walk.

«Would you like to talk, like we do sometimes, about your feelings?»

«Yes.»

«You were psychotic yesterday. You usually get like that when you have problems on your mind. When you've been thinking about your life. Have you been having these sorts of thoughts recently?»

«Yes, lots.»

We don't speak, and then Tobias repeats:

«Yes, lots.»

«Sex, finding a woman … how to go about it?»

«Yes.»

Tobias is quiet, thinking. Me too. I am trying to intuit just how he is thinking.

«Are you wondering about your chances? That it is difficult to interest a woman when you have aphasia? How can one be attractive without the power of words?»

«Yes, that's right.»

I think. I try to put the puzzle together. The TV channel – porn – stimulation – awakened sexual desire – masturbation – doubts arise – he feels alone and single and feels at odds with the situation … he would rather have a girlfriend … he is longing for love.

My thoughts turn to Café Zenit. This lies closest to hand in my inner thought processes around the subject of girls – flirting – togetherness – eyeing – being in love.

I describe this dilemma for Tobias.

«Can this be it? Sexual desire, relief in solitude … this collides with your desire for a girl of your own (Tobias' word is girl).»

«Yes, yes, that's right.»

You have a right to long. You are longing for love. That's it, that's just it.

Silence, then in a stronger tone:

«Yes … yes!»

I think again. Give a piece of advice.

«You must keep things separate. You have sexual needs that are physical and natural. You can make use of the films in order to satisfy your physical needs. You can keep this apart from love. You are longing for love. That is a different matter. You should see this as a different area … where longing is.»

I draw squares in the air to illustrate different areas, with sex in one and love in the other. He looks at the «squares».

Tobias is quiet, thinking.

«Yes. Good. Thanks.»

He understands what I mean and seems to agree.

155

MOURNING TAKES VARYING LENGTHS OF TIME

As I have mentioned, I lecture quite a lot on crisis and grief, reactions within different phases and about the various stages of a crisis. I mentioned it in my earlier book and I will recapitulate in short now.

Crises come in a variety of forms. They can be caused by trauma such as the loss of a loved one, a limb, a skill, and material security as well as well-known crises such as development crises, identity crises, and life crises.

What Johan Cullberg calls «the natural process of a crisis» applies mainly to those crises that occur through trauma. The crises threaten ingrained conceptions concerning security and identity, i.e. who one is in the context of one's relations. One loses the sense of controlling one's own life. Examples of trauma that can trigger crises are; losses (death, illness, divorce etcetera), insults (abandonment, mobbing, dismissal), and catastrophes (where the crisis does not only affect the person directly concerned but even close friends and relatives) (Cullberg, 2006).

Cullberg's phase theory consists of four phases or stages: Shock/acute-phase, Reaction-phase, «working-through» and «reorientation».

The first phase, the shock/acute-phase, arises during very violent and unexpectedly dramatic events. This stage usually lasts up to two days. The function of this phase is to protect us from panic; emotions have to wait so that we can survive by keeping a cool head or waiting things out. In the acute phase, the rug has been pulled out from under your feet. The very foundation you have been standing on, the safe base from which everyday matters have been handled is no longer there. Something has changed or been taken away, and you don't know how to cope with it, if it can be coped with, and what the consequences will be. You experience an uncertainty that is confusing and strange. Depending upon your personality and what kind of previous experiences you have had of coping with adversity, loss or confusing changes, the reaction will be individual. Many can react with denial, others scream out their pain, while others become energetically practical or totally, helplessly dejected.

All that one can do to help someone in this phase is basically to just be there, perhaps hold them tight, sit quietly, cook some food for them or in other ways help them with small practical things. As people in this phase lose all sense of time, hunger and thirst, it can be of enormous worth to make sure that food and drink are available at regular intervals.

In this phase, we can only accept support and information that gives us hope for survival. Smalltalk can obstruct and cause confusion. One is in a practical survival-phase and therefore disinclined to social interaction, which in turn can cause conflicts and misunderstandings.

The second phase, the reaction-phase, comes when the shock has passed and the person feels safe enough to feel, experience, and think about what has happened. This is when you regain access to your feelings, the various defence mechanisms disappear and the pain can be felt! This phase is supposed to last for a few months, but I have seen people in it for years, especially if the incident provided new challenges and problems without end as is the case with a family member's illness or injury. As the reactions tend to be strong, adrenaline will be produced, releasing energy to fight in order to get rid of the appalling, the unbearable. This alert state of readiness to react will sometimes lead to insomnia, loss of appetite, pain, anxiety and irritability. If one passes through and out of the reaction phase, a processing will start and one finds oneself calmer and rather more relaxed.

The reaction-phase needs a phase-specific treatment. In this phase; talking, describing, and telling are options for the affected person, especially if people show an interest. We can

157

help the person in question by still being able to sit with them in silence but also by managing to listen to them go through the event time and time again. This helps the person to let off steam and strengthens her ability to accept her heavy feelings. Defence mechanisms and sleeping difficulties can be found in this phase as well, and this might call for professional help in order to let go of defences and find trust in the healing power of sleep and companionship.

The third phase is Working Through. You process the experience. This can take between six months and a year. However, I have met with many people who have mourned for many years without there being any signs of rigidity, denial or that they were stuck in any way. It is important that each and everyone must be allowed the time they need and respect the fact that tears and despair can be interlaced with joy and thankfulness. One can be surprised by the fact that sensitivity can be an enriching life-giving force and not necessarily a burden that one just has to carry till it disappears. Working Through is a psychoanalytic concept. My understanding of it is that thoughts and feelings alternate, the energy from feelings feeds reflections as to what the changes involve in different respects. Thoughts inspire us to formulate and understand that a change is taking place, and that one can both feel and talk about it, or if you are a loner, think about it, and draw conclusions about the consequences of what has happened at home, at work, among friends, in spare time etcetera, all depending upon the nature of the crisis.

As one approaches the fourth phase; the re-orientation phase, your thoughts turn to the future and you start planning with the insight that you cannot regain the time and whatever else it is that has been lost. This can be a life-long phase, as memories of a valuable time together, or an existence, can result in an eternal feeling of now, a feeling that one neither can, nor want to, or even need to let go of. The pain is no longer strong or frequent, even if it can still make its appearance in situations that remind us of the person, thing or context that has been lost.

Not all crises pass over completely, especially the grief that parents feel for a lost child, or when a family member is debilitated after an accident causing brain-damage or an illness with an uncertain prognosis. The way in which you cope with and process a crisis depends largely upon your life situation, your mental ability to cope with adversities, and whether you have a real, secure and trustworthy relationship with other people. Those who do not have this can sometimes also cope with loneliness, even though it has been shown that the lonely people who manage best actually do feel they have some kind of relationship, be it with a pet perhaps, or with some more abstract figure, for instance a divinity. These days, one can even blog with anonymous strangers, though I have no idea what kind of support this can offer. I do believe, however, that physical closeness is of invaluable support in a crisis.

Sometimes, people don't come through a crisis in a healthy way. They experience anxiety, are aggressive and difficult to cope with, they are more than usually physically sick, chronically tired and suffer from insomnia over a longer period of time.

Some of the reactions to crisis that might require professional help include: States of disorientation and reactive psychoses, intractable anxiety and depression. Let's not be imprecise with the definition of depression. To be distressed, sad, very angry or in the grip of a powerful longing, to wonder about the meaning of life and to sometimes feel that one would just like to sleep, that one has no desire to talk to anyone or adversely feel that one cannot be alone – this is what I call grief, not depression. In those instances friends can give just enough support. But not being able to reach one's deeper feelings, not being able to feel the emptiness of longing or the bitter-sweet taste of loss, but rather to feel frighteningly, strangely empty, haunted by an unbearable pain, or a longing for death, this is depression and in those instances I recommend psychotherapy. If there is no relief or feeling of hope within a few weeks of therapy once or twice a week, then I would recommend changing the psychotherapist as this can be because the necessary feeling of trust is missing. If trust exists and the therapist is felt to be professional, competent and safe to trust, but the depression continues to be unbearable, a visit to a psychiatrist may be of help. Medication for a while might be needed in order to come up from the deepest darkness while simultaneously working with a psychotherapist or psychologist.

I shall spend a little time dealing with grief and mourning, as these are essential parts of life. Those that have no cause to mourn have never been so close to anyone that loss has been felt. Sorrow is the price one pays for love, and without love there will be no sorrow. Loss and mourning, the feeling that someone or something has been ripped away is always a very strong experience.

Tore and I are sitting, talking. It would seem that for the first time, Tore is properly mourning the Tobias we had and the effects of the brain-damage. This comes up when I mention that I and my friend, Lill, are planning to go on a bicycle holiday for a few days. I have asked Tore if this is okay, just as one does in that phase of life when one has small children to care for. We have Tobias. Tore says that it is fine.

The subject has come up again and I mention that I am considering taking the holiday in late August when Tobias has returned to his normal weekly routine, and it will only be a question of Tore being alone with Tobias on Saturday and Sunday.

Yes, thinks Tore, because it will be like déjà-vu if I go in the middle of the holiday period when Tobias is with him full-time. By which Tore means that it will mean reliving an earlier experience, and this gives him a feeling of unease. I realize that he is afraid of a repetition of earlier periods when I have been away. Once on a job trip and another on a recreational journey and both times Tobias became psychotic. Furthermore, Tore has freed up more time to look after Tobias during a crisis than I have. For the past few years, Tore has been working from home more than I have, with the consequence that we have agreed that Tore is in a better position to take time out and with fewer consequences for third parties (clients).

Tore is traumatised, this we agree upon. He feels an almost constant mental readiness to look after Tobias. It was difficult for him last week, and I notice that he feels vulnerable when he hints that he takes on more of the burden than I do.

Tore is sometimes away on his own business, too, even though this has become less frequent. I regret this fact. I wish that he did things for his own sake more often. I would support him, and he knows this. This is the way we have to live nowadays; we can't travel together just like that. These last eleven years, Tobias has been frail and can become psychotic if we (especially I) are absent. One might look upon this as being over-protective if one is not familiar with such a situation, or have personal experiences of living with a mentally disabled person.

However, facts speak for themselves. When Tore and I were in Cuba in 2001 for two weeks, Tobias went into one of his first really strong psychoses. When we tried to make a new attempt several years later by holidaying on Sardinia, we had to break off the trip and travel home as Tobias had become totally regressed and neither ate, drank, or slept and was incontinent, catatonic and crazy in every possible way.

He travelled with us to Nepal this year (2008), two weeks in May, and despite masses of impressions, which can be difficult for a person with brain-damage to cope with, Tobias felt well the whole time. However, Tore became weary of being Tobias' assistant. This was Tore's job as I was taking part in a conference which was why we made the journey in the first place.

So here we are, talking, my dear husband and I.

I ask Tore about his grief. Whereabouts does he find himself? He feels more sorrow now than at any time since the accident. He is no longer running from it. He tried to avoid his sorrow, earlier. He became restless and he feels that he smoked and ate excessively, as an escape.

He is no longer running from it.

«I am in mourning, that's what it is, there is no getting away from it. I'm not trying to either.»

I think that Tore ought to go in therapy. He says it's easier just to talk with me.

But I'm also affected.

«No, you have come out of mourning, out into the sunshine on the other side,» says Tore.

«No, I haven't.»

But I mourned more those first years. Everything was black. Now I have days, though mostly only moments, of sadness and sometimes I am angry about our restricted life.

But then I compare us with others that are worse off. They are there; the parents of a drug addict who refuses to stop, or a heavily criminalized person who refuses to change …

REFERENCE

Cullberg, J. (2006) *Kris och Utveckling. Samt Katastrofpsykiatri och sena stressreaktioner* Sthlm: Natur & Kultur.

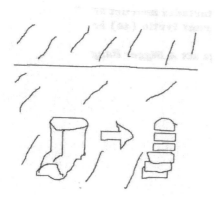

Drawing by Tobias

A TALK IN THE GARDEN

Tobias and I are in a talkative mood. Last night, he had a very powerful epileptic seizure and today, he is unusually lively and talkative. Strange. It was a dramatic attack. The whole of his left side had powerful cramps, his left leg pointed up towards the ceiling, his right arm was stiffly bent but shook, the whole of the left part of his body and parts of the right shook violently, the whites of his eyes were pink, while his eyes flickered towards the right, and there were the typical sounds coming from his throat. We performed the usual procedure that has become a routine if we have luck and are awakened by the attack. Attacks only occur at night, in deep sleep, because a couple of years after he got the brain damage, I taught Tobias to control the attacks when awake. We always have a radio receiver in our room, a «baby-sitter». However, when Tobias is alone in his own flat, as he is weekdays, then we must put up with the risk, which his self-voluntary solitude involves.

When people hear about this we always get lots of advice. None of it is realistic in Tobias' case. He feels secure in his flat, he doesn't want to move. He wants to sleep alone in his one room. He can't have a vibration alarm affixed to his bed, since he must be allowed to satisfy his sexual needs, or go to the toilet, without the SOS people coming in and interrupting whatever it is he's doing. Which adult would want that?

Anyway, here we are in the sun with our coffee. Tobias is enjoying himself. Initially, the conversation is about whether Tobias is happy staying with us. It is Tobias who opens the subject.

«Ok … and you?»

«If it is ok with me that you spend your free time here?»

163

«Yes?»

«Yes, it's perfectly okay with me that you live here. You are an adult with thoughts of your own. I'm grateful that you enjoy staying with us. I can't take for granted that you would.»

«No?» (His tone of voice betrays interest)

«No, not everybody enjoys staying with their parents.»

Tobias' facial expression expresses agreement. I tell him about my father, who was single after the divorce from my mother, when Tobias and Mårten were small, and how his living with us for a few years worked out. I compare this to how well Tobias' staying with us works.

Tobias praises me, saying I am good. He says:

«You and me, different and the same. More and less. Though more and more like this.»

Tobias hand is wide open, and he clenches it slowly, while at the same time, showing with his arm how strong he becomes.

«You and me … strong! Good!»

Silence.

«Hmm, have you thought about the possibility of me dying? Tore and I will most probably die before you.»

«Yes.»

«At what age do you think I may die? How old will I be when I die?»

After a silent pause, Tobias writes in the air: 300.

«300 years?»

«Yes.»

«Impossible.»

«No! Earlier, yes, but later.»

«Oh, our DNA can't live that long. Let's be realistic! Maybe I take after my mom and dad. If nothing unexpected happens – I mean, I can be hit by a car, or have an accident.»

«Yes.»

Tobias gives me an understanding look.

«But if I have luck and avoid that sort of thing, than my father has very good genes. His father, uncles and aunts, have lived to at least 90 years, several of them. Dad is addicted to alcohol; he has been wearing out his heart and liver, so maybe he won't last so long. He's 81 now.»

«A pity»

«Yes. But I probably have his genes. And I live soundly. My mother is 74 years old now, soon 75. She looks as if she's 60, and is very energetic. She can also live a long life. Though, maybe she'll have problems with her health because of worry. She has a tendency towards worry. I manage life better than my parents so I have good prospects for a long life.»

Silence.

«If I live till I'm 100 years old, then you'll be 80 then.»

«Yes.»

«When I'm 100 you'll most likely think it's okay if I die.»

«Yes, think so.»

«By then you maybe have a wife.»

«Yes, good, just like that.»

«Tore is strong too, but he worries.»

«What? What do you mean?»

«He worries about your future. Your economy, about being able to go out for a coffee, to have personal assistance etcetera …»

«But, better and better. Like this» (he shows me how his body shakes) «and fantastic» (and points to the left side of his head).

«Do you mean that the brain creates connections after an attack?»

«Yes,» he says emphatically.

«Hmm-mm?»

«You don't believe it? I know!!!»

«You're sure then?»

«Yes!!! Sure!!!»

«Hmm, yes, you have some kind of body-knowledge. You probably know best.»

«Where's Tobbe?» asks Tore.

«He went and lay down on his bed.»

We go in to see how he's feeling.

«Feeling low?»

«No. Just sweaty.»

«Yes, it's a warm day, makes you dozy. May I lie down beside you?»

«Yes.»

Tobias moves over a little. He says:

«You are good.»

He puts out his hand in order to stroke me, happens to get close to my breast, and quickly withdraws his hand:

«Oops, sorry!»

«You just wanted to touch me and you can't see to the right or where your hand gets. Nothing to worry about.»

Silence.

«Tore?»

«Where's Tore? He's on the porch, smoking, leaning on the rail and looking at the trees, enjoying himself.»

«Good.»

«You are … good, not only, you're also …»

With his hand he makes a sparkling movement by his head.

«Do you mean my head sparkles … do you mean bright?»

«Yes, bright, good. I also bright. Me and Tore. Yes, and … Mårten.»

«Yes, what a bright family! Four bright people. Here comes one of the brights.»

«Yes,» says Tobias and reaches out a hand to Tore who has just come in at the door.

Just when Tobias reaches out his hand towards Tore, Tore says:

«I'll take a shower now.»

«Well …. (commandingly) No! Sure! Ok!»

Laughter.

There is so much love. It's so wonderful with holidays. Just to lie on the bed, or the beach or the lawn beside Tobias and to divine his thoughts. He often reflects about himself, his life, his identity, and his relationships. More often than most of us have reason to.

Is Tobias unusually talented, having such grave brain damage?

Yes, and so uneven. That such a deeply thoughtful person can also have grave aphasia, a weak memory, an inability to plan, apraxia, etcetera, is so hard to fathom. Those who see him out walking, who say «Hi» and have a chat cannot understand that the same young man can stand for fifteen minutes wondering what the word «wallet» means.

Love is strong and I discover during my holidays, when time is no problem, that I can appreciate Tobias and his calm tempo without any reservations whatsoever.

Our society is wrong, our demands for efficiency are wrong. Efficiency gives no life quality in itself. Without the timeless togetherness that Tobias is capable of, life seems pretty pointless. Those people who don't have this timeless togetherness can never really feel well.

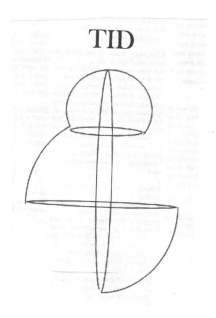

«TIME» Drawing by
Tobias

GUESSES AND HOPES

I have been away on official business for the last ten days. First, I was in Italy, from Thursday to Monday. Things went well for Tore at home with Tobias. Then I travelled to Vienna for a conference. On Friday, Tore rings and says:

«The storm has broken, here at home.»

I understand his meaning. Tobias is the storm. It is cold both at home and in Vienna during my days at the conference, the 16th – 20th of September, 2008. The chilly weather is the harbinger of colds and Tobias has had a fever. Fever is a curse for a damaged brain, or at least for Tobias' brain. He goes crazy. My absence is also a strain, one that is perhaps just too much for him. Motherlessness and fever equals storm.

Tore will have to cope with him. Tobias is in regression and psychotic. He is sensitive to sudden touch, compulsive as regards food and drink, anxious and in need of constant reassurance and care every single minute, without respite. He needs a Nozinan at night but, during the day, Tore's intensive presence does the job. This is progress compared to earlier psychoses.

As I have mentioned earlier, the level of regression, the flights from reality and delusions in each psychosis seem to lie at progressively less primitive levels. It is no longer necessary for Tobias to be a hero in Star Wars or to build a new civilization on another planet. Now it is a question of Tobias receiving help with an annihilation-anxiety that at times is relieved via aggressive behaviour and opposition to everything we suggest. But this is in fact better than when he wanted to fight or escape, or, like one of the first times, when he not only wanted to escape himself but to bring all the passengers on the tram with him as well, upsetting the driver who could neither close the doors or continue the journey. His assistant pulled Tobias off the tram with violence that time.

Now, I'm tired after the long lecture tour and remember Tore's words before I left, when he saw my massive congress schedule:
«You can have a rest when you come home on Saturday.»

Yes, I have a free morning on Monday. Tore is exhausted. He has neither managed to clean or wash, had no time to vacuum floors, clean tables, kitchen worktops or the bathroom. The grass on the lawn is a decimetre tall. These are worldly things, and I will have to ignore home and garden for the moment. However, congress-tired and travel-weary as I am, I cannot avoid reacting to the sight of the mess, I cannot ward off a number of fleeting clouds of worry: What if I must learn to live with a situation where we never have time to maintain our home or garden? It makes me slightly afraid, and a tiny, tiny voice at the back of my head says anxiously:
«Imagine things always being like this; what if Tobias becomes chronically schizophrenic?» But this is only a tiny, anxious voice. A stronger voice says:
«Attend to his developments! See how Tobias has come through psychosis after psychosis, with an ever greater speed of recovery, and a diminishing number of difficulties. And in-between! He is a miracle of patience and charm.»

But not just now.
I spend Monday morning giving Tobias all my love and attention. Tore moves his afternoon work in town to Tuesday and I go in to work in the afternoon. On Tuesday, Tore and Tobias go in to town together, and Tobias seems calm enough to be able to live in his flat, with the help of his assistants.

At 6.15 on Wednesday morning, the telephone rings in Brännö. I answer, sleepily. I usually sleep between 22.30 and 07.30. It is one of Tobias' neighbours who is calling, saying that another neighbour has seen Tobias out on the street and helped him into the house as he had no key with him. He's in his stocking-feet and is really cold. He is now sitting on the stairs. The neighbour wonders what to do. I ask her whether she can possibly make sure that Tobias doesn't wander away, while I try to arrange for someone to come.

Neighbours can be wonderful. This neighbour is. She asks her son to go over to Tobias. I phone Anders, who is Tobias' assistant today and who, thank God, lives in the same neighbourhood. He goes there.

Tobias had left his flat via the balcony, without his shoes. Who knows what he was thinking of? Maybe he was missing the summer, and, feeling rested, he wanted to try to revive a little summer feeling out on the balcony steps. The day before, you see, he had enjoyed our time, sitting on the porch on Brännö. I got the feeling that he wanted to hold on to the «summer with mom and dad» feeling. Perhaps he was missing us? I know, these are just speculations.

When Anders arrives, he does his best to find out what has happened. Tobias shows him that he had awoken during the night and walked down to Masthuggstorget, a square close to the fitness centre where he usually goes training.

After a little while, Anders discovers that Tobias' wallet is missing. Imagine if he has been robbed during the night? A man walking around in his socks, seemingly remote and maybe not answering questions, is probably an ideal victim? His wallet was in his jeans last night and he was wearing these jeans on his nightly escapade. Or did he leave the balcony door open when he set off? This door leads straight onto the communal lawn. Did a thief slip through the door and steal his wallet from his jeans, hanging over the back of his sofa? Maybe Tobias was awakened by the thief and set out to follow him?

We will never know why he went out, and perhaps he doesn't even know himself. He doesn't remember in any case. However, he does remember where he went, and that is good. When we discuss this incident, Tobias agrees that it wasn't a very adequate behaviour. To go out in the middle of the night without proper clothing is not good. Besides, it is well known that young men run the risk of being mugged in the middle of the night, a more and more common risk in our city. But I haven't the energy to care, I haven't the energy to manage with the normal worries that parents have for their sons and daughters out having fun at night. I can only afford that special worry, caused by Tobias being unable to clothe himself correctly, thus catching cold, getting fever, and becoming crazy. That we will become more and more captive. I can't imagine that, I can't accept this sort of scenario. It is just not possible for our family to be more restricted than it already is. One cannot live like that. That's how I feel right now.

However, before Tobias' accident, I had no idea that we would be able to manage what we have already managed. If someone had told me how his life would come to be changed, I would have said:

«I couldn't manage that. I'd go mad.»

Luckily, I did not know that my eldest son would lose half of his vision, almost all of his speech, all of his reading and writing abilities, large parts of his movement functions, large parts of his memory - especially the semantic and the abstract, his planning capacity (the little he had), his independence and his theoretical, logic intelligence.

171

But one can live with it! One can relate to it. It's now a question of finding some kind of quality of life within this life. He has a right to a good life, and we try to have one, too. We already have a good life. In fact we do.

Tobias' younger brother must be allowed to enjoy his own family, enjoy his vigorous life, with two healthy children and a wonderful wife. I need to have my work, my leisure, my friends, my husband and our moments, just the two of us.

It is all about this «now». It is about being there during these acute phases, when everything else seems secondary and Tobias' anxiety has to be lessened, with as much love as we can give him, and as little medicine as is humanly possible, since the medicines wear out a damaged brain. At the moment, it is 25 mg Nozinan before night, those first three or four days while the madness sits like a cement wall around his awareness, a wall that gives his mental distortions free rein. But, we don't allow more medicine than this. His body smells of garbage and his breathe smells like a sewer several days after Nozinan treatment.

Or, is it rather the psychosis itself that produces these unpleasant smells? Who knows? I recognize these vapours from my time working within psychiatric care, but this gives no answer to the question of what is the cause of this smell: mood or medicine.

Tobias consumes a relatively small dose of medicine, generally. A few neuroleptic pills per quarter year and diazepam when needed, and it may be several months between doses.

Today, Thursday, I am sitting in my office writing this when Mårten phones. Guesses and hopes are the order of the day this week. Mårten was in Halmstad[14] earlier today when Glenn, Tobias' assistant, called him up for advice. This morning, he and Tobias had been on the way to the shoe-maker's

---

14 A town, 100 miles south of Göteborg.

shop, when Tobias demanded that they continue their tram journey to where Mårten lives, to say hello. When they found out that Mårten was not at home, since there was no answer from the home telephone, Tobias demanded to go up to his street door, anyway. Once there, Glenn couldn't stop him ringing on one of the door-bells. Not Carolusson's though, but Tidell's. Tobias refused to believe Glenn's assurance that Mårten was in Halmstad.

Mårten phones me to ask if I can leave my office for a while in order to help Glenn and Tobias. I cycle over to Mårten's street door but Glenn and Tobias aren't there. Glenn can't answer his mobile telephone since Tobias has confiscated it in a rather aggressive manner. However, after a little while, Glenn manages to trick Tobias and can send a text, saying that they are now on a new adventure, this time a stroll in Vasa Church, a few minutes away. I cycle over, and Tobias is now very calm. We sit and chat in the sun on the church steps. I mention my theory about fever and today's craziness and Glenn confirms this view. Tobias had been shivering on the way to the city, and he is still sweaty. Quite understandable, considering how cold he had been two nights ago. Fever gives Tobias psychosis. He's very happy to see me and assumes that I will take over from Glenn right there on the church steps. Tobias looks disappointed when I tell him that I have to cycle to Mölndal (8 km away), to supervise a group there.

«Why?» he asks.

«Do you feel that I have been away a lot recently?» I reply, and he agrees.

I promise to cycle home to Tobias directly after work. I can be there just after half past four. Tobias looks closely into my eyes and asks:

«Certain?»

I answer:

«Do I usually trick you?»

«No»

«No, you can be certain that I will come.»

He seems calm. I cycle off after giving him two pills of Treo, the only antipyretics I could find in my office, though I would rather have found a pill without a bracing additive, which would be more suitable for somebody already agitated.

Suddenly, I can see something in Tobias' eyes that I recognize from other times when he's been out of balance; anger, independence, scorn. Weak, weak, and yet. I interpret his look, and ask him if he's feeling a need to be independent right now, and he answers «yes». I compare it with how he probably felt the other night. He just wanted to go out and take a walk by himself. He's angry now at the fact that Glenn is an assistant, which reminds him of his unwanted situation. I affirm that he doesn't want to have assistants, really, as he doesn't want to be in a situation where he needs help. He agrees. I tell him how interesting his art is and what a good artist he has become and that this is something he has gained from his accident. He listens and seems to think it over and then asks if it is really so.

«Yes.»

Glenn helps too, saying that he doesn't really feel like an assistant, and that he would rather see himself as a friend. We talk about it a while, the fact that Tobias can only have assistants that could just as well have been his friends. Everything seems calm now and I set off.

I don't know whether it is the stimulating effect of the antipyretics or my leaving (a reminder of the longer one quite recently) that makes Tobias even more aggressive towards Glenn at this point, and to go directly back to Mårten's street-door. Once again, it is Tidell's bell he wants to ring. Glenn phones to Mårten, who makes the very clever guess that Tobias, with his aphasia, believes that the name on the bell is Wadell. Wadell is the name of a family that Tobias really likes, and has known for a long time, from long before the accident. Mårten gives Glenn this hint. It seems to be so. Via the telephone,

Marten advises Glenn to suggest to Tobias that «as we don't quite know where in town the Wadell family lives» perhaps they should go home and check their address on the Internet.

Tobias agrees to this plan, although the tram trip is a severe test for Glenn. He has to keep away from Tobias so as not to irritate him, while Tobias greets and approaches everyone he feels he wants to be best friends with. But, they manage to get home, and Tore gets there very soon, too. Tore then persuades Tobias to come with him out to Brännö.

Mårten, this wonderful younger brother, immediately realizes the importance of calling all the assistants to a meeting, so that they can talk everything over, and get understanding and support in order to be able to continue in good heart, boosted by each other and by Mårten.

How can one supervise assistants and at the same time be the brother of the client? It is not totally apparent that this is

The Assistant Glenn and Tobias

175

the best solution, and I have seen many examples of cases where it has been very unsuitable.

However, viewing Mårten's actions from all angles, he proves time and again that it is hard to imagine a more suitable supervisor for Tobias' assistants.

Yes, of course! I can now see the answer to the question that has been asked, between the lines, throughout the whole of this chapter: «How does one manage?» And the answer is: Whatever we possess that can be used to give Tobias a good life, must be given. This attitude, or maybe it is a question of values, gives strength. At times, though, it would have been nice to do without.

MADNESS OR PTSD

One cannot always expect a deeper level of understanding from medical experts. I have tried. My own expertise is far too extensive for me to expect especially much from the broader phalanx of neurology. The problem with the experts is not any lack of knowledge or competence. The problem is their lack of sensitivity and humility. As a relative, I have a motivation to learn everything about brain damage, with a learning rate that is seldom found in one's own more neutral, professional role. Doctors ought to have noticed by now just how much the devoted relatives manage to learn about their family member's predicament, even if they don't have a health care profession themselves. I have a health care profession, and two professional licences, so it is not surprising that I had no difficulties in achieving a high level of knowledge about everything that has to do with the functions of the brain. So, why doesn't Tobias' neurologist appreciate my competence? What does he have to lose by seeing us as participants with the same interest – the very best for Tobias?

My previous book about Tobias presented many or according to its critics, far too many examples of authoritarian conduct from health care staff, which in my mind should be replaced by a perceptive, respectful communication. At the time of writing the present book, I have got over my disappointment and my illusions. This is why this book concentrates more upon what I have to say about psychological treatment. These days, I expect nothing from the health service; we, the family and assistants take care of Tobias' needs, in even the most difficult situations. We have become a fantastic team: Tobias' brother and assistants, we parents, the Feldenkrais pedagogue who has followed Tobias for many years, and during the last few years, Tobias teacher and psychologist who work with Tobias via art therapy. My experience of daily activity and habilitation has been positive. They don't suffer from the meaningless prestige that I have met within the world of medicine. One important exception is intensive care, of which I wrote about earlier. The staff there had an admirable humility, flexibility, a deep sense of responsibility and professionalism. However, for pedagogical reasons, I would now like to give an example of prestige and authority.

One Monday, Tobias visited his neurologist, who had taken over the practice of his predecessor, who had been caring and kind, but not as knowledgeable about the practical consequences of brain damage as one would have expected of a neurologist. However, of greater importance was the fact that he showed that he liked Tobias; he asked us questions about things he didn't understand and, in parenthesis, other patients have told me that he had my first book visible on his desk for the other patients and relatives to see. His successor was focused and attentive to Tobias, who in turn liked this attention and felt respected. I was with Tobias at a visit to this doctor at one occasion, and six months before the one I shall soon describe. In this meeting I described Tobias' psychotic episodes – the doctor reacted then with raised eyebrows, and informed me with obvious authority that the diagnosing of psychosis is very special and asked me haughtily to explain. I did so, with a large number of symptom descriptions and the doctor immediately retreated and said «yes, yes, that's correct».

Six months later, the assistant Jörgen, was with Tobias at the doctor, and I was not. I had enclosed a note concerning the fact that Lyrica, for epilepsy, had been tested since January without giving rise to any noticeable side-effects (yet, it came half a year later, as described in a previous chapter). I also recorded that the side effect of day-tiredness had disappeared since, at my initiative and with the doctor's consent, we had skipped the morning dosage, keeping only the evening dose. The frequency of epilepsy attacks at night (since I taught him self-hypnosis, daytime attacks had ceased, as he had learned to control them) was unaffected unfortunately, but the psychotic behaviour had eased during the year and, as this may be related to the medicine, I suggested that Tobias should perhaps continue so for a while.

That is what I wrote.

To Jörgen and Tobias, the doctor said:

«What does she mean by the word psychotic? She can't use that term without an explanation. She will have to write and explain what she means. Ask her to do that.»

Jörgen replied that Susanna is qualified and knows the definition of psychosis, so she is most certainly using the term correctly. The doctor replied that she, Susanna, is only a behavioural scientist, and as such has no right to make such a diagnosis. Jörgen described Tobias' planet fantasies, his omnipotent delusions, hallucinations, mania, etcetera, until the doctor finally said: «Ok, she doesn't need to write and explain, then».

Jörgen then asked the doctor whether Tobias will ever be able to steer his right arm, whether the nerves can create connections, to which the doctor replied, «No». Tobias looked sharply at the doctor and said «Yes!»

He knows that, ten years after losing those areas of the cortex that steer the muscles of the right side of the body, he has learnt to bend his right foot to an angle. This was impossible a year earlier, nine years after the injury!

This doctor now produced the dismal suggestion that the brain cells of people with brain damage degenerate more rapidly than normal, with the consequence that the dosage of medicine needs to be raised over the years.

Yes, this may be the case for those brain damaged people who, owing to avoidance mechanisms, keep away from stimulation that provokes and challenges the disability. However, if one is brave, like Tobias, one widens one's perspective and continually processes, with ever growing awareness and insight with an enriched interaction with one's surroundings as a result. It is well-known that such a process counteracts the degeneration of the brain. If this can be true for Tobias, with a large scar in his brain but absolutely no degenerative illness, then there can be no, absolutely no reason to believe that medication dosage must be raised over time, rather the opposite. Even if I am wrong, it is still an unnecessary suggestion that will be proved true owing to the fact that patients trust the authority of doctors! This is called «expectation effect» in psychological terminology.

I felt the need to mail a little information about how diagnostic competence is a part of my profession, as I will explain to you here, too.

One becomes a behavioural scientist (that is what the neurologist called me) by taking a Bachelor of Science degree in psychology, sociology, pedagogy, and the philosophy of science together with an academic paper. I have two clinical exams in the health and care area. I have the exam as a psychologist with a psychology license, which in its earlier form (which I studied) demanded up to 8 years university studies, including work practice. Afterwards, I had 2 years apprenticeship before I took my next degree in psychotherapy and gained that license, too.

Both of my licences demand of me that I make a psychological and psychiatric diagnosis. The National Board of Health gives me independent responsibility to examine, diagnose and treat patients. Behavioural scientists do not have this competence or jurisdiction.

The art of diagnosing someone as psychotic depends upon a number of specific symptoms, and is not at all difficult to do. Anyone who has lived at close range to a psychotic person would agree. To understand the real meaning behind the symptoms of a psychosis is more complicated and demands that one either has deep personal knowledge, a natural talent, or psychological and psychodynamic knowledge. If one regards the psychosis' forms of expression as behaviour without meaning, then the impression will be so bizarre and its understanding so elusive that one can only see madness. With a deeper knowledge and an investigative, analytical mind, one can see beyond this madness.

Tobias has behaved in a strange way for several days. On Wednesday, he laughed madly at the wrong time, according to his assistant that day. During the following days, Tobias had difficulty understanding nouns, difficulty in performing routine tasks that usually caused no problems, and he was in need of being close to his family, especially Tore.

On Saturday, Tore and I were to go into the city to have dinner. An assistant who is very calm and stable was going to be at home in our house with Tobias while we were away. They spent their time watching a film, eating dinner, washing up, and Tobias phoned to us every ten minutes. We thus realized that Tobias was upset, and decided to go home to him earlier than planned.

He was in obvious need of us. Why? This, of course, is what we discussed on the way home and hopefully we would soon find out the reason. We always try to see context. We can usually understand Tobias, when the pieces of puzzle are sufficiently clear.

When we arrive at Brännö, Tobias and his assistant are there to meet us. They are on the landing stage, waiting. The assistant can take the same boat back to Saltholmen on the mainland. The alternative for him would have been to take a midnight boat – not attractive for any of us. I strongly feel that I want to focus all my attention to Tobias.

When we are finally home, a sense of security settles upon us, and the atmosphere is calm enough for us to facilitate a state of drowsiness and sleep. Tobias falls asleep.

It is Sunday. The morning has consisted of a quiet, peaceful breakfast that didn't put any demands upon Tobias. We give him full service, aiming at creating a calm security without any provocative tests. Tobias looks at his watch. He looks surprised and fascinated. Yes, unfortunately, for us, his attitude appears to be a little bit crazy. He has that stubborn attitude, unyielding, yes, as if he would simply die if he can't perform that magic trick, the trick that I can never understand or know …

I ask him if there is anything special about the time being two o'clock.
    «Two? Zero zero.»
    I imagine that zero zero means start, zero-mode, but normalize the question by asking instead whether Tobias wishes it was 12 o'clock.
    «Yes.»
    But there is a hesitation in his voice.
    I ask:
    «Midday? Zero zero. Noon?»
    Tobias repeats:
    «Noon.»

He is silent for a while. He points to my watch. He wants me to take it off. I feel that this is something that I would rather lead Tobias away from. But I have learnt to understand that in situations such as this, Tobias needs respect. And that respect, no matter how crazy his behaviour seems to be, can lead to a deeper understanding of what has been the cause of this seemingly bizarre behaviour.

I search within myself after possible explanations of the incidents of the last week. However, I can find nothing that can have offended or worried Tobias and his self-esteem. Quite the opposite, Tobias seems to be in a harmonic phase, despite the regressive dependence upon us these last few days. Intuitively, I feel that this is not the time to play detective and search for connections in the last week's events.

Tobias looks at me and says:

«Two.»

«Aha, what does that mean?»

I try everything. Two. The time is in fact two o'clock.

He says:

«Minutes.»

I don't really want to take this about minutes seriously. Tobias shows that this is something personal. I read this as a desire that it was some other time of day, like noon, for example. I talk about the necessity that we all have of a synchronized time in order that things like timetables work. Tobias repeats the word «minutes» and says:

«Two?»

Then he says:

«Bye bye.»

«Are you going to die again?»

«Yes.»

«No, not again,» I think. Good God, release him from this now. Tobias seems calm and not at all worried. His hand is sweaty, though, which means that his brain is stressed.

A symptom of epileptic activity? Does it remind him of his state of unconsciousness twelve years ago, when he was dead a short while?

Tobias looks at me and repeats the words «two minutes» and from his tone of voice I hear that it is a question. I ask:

«Are you wondering if you were dead for two minutes, then? The 2nd of August 1996?»

«Yes!»

«Yes, maybe you were.«

«Yes,» says Tobias and goes off to bed in his room, to die.

I explain that he is experiencing his body-memory of dying, and he agrees. I explain to him that when body-memory is activated, it feels as if the event is happening right now. That is why he is certain he is going to die at this moment. However, in actual fact it is an old event that lies twelve years in the past. The brain doesn't understand this, however.

Tobias listens and understands. And knows that in two minutes he is going to die. And then wake up. Just like then.

I ask him if he wants to die alone or if he wants me to be with him? He wants to be alone.

I don't want him to be alone in this state.

When he has gone to his room, I follow and ask him if I may join him anyway, and explain that I am curious as to how his reliving the episode of dying and revival will look like.

He lets me, and asks me to help him push the cat from his bed first. It is not suitable having her there just now.

I do so. I sit beside him and check his pulse. He lies there staring at the ceiling.

«Do you understand? Twelve years ago you were dead, and now you are re-enacting it?»

«Yes.»

Silence.

«Wow, wow, wow!» cries Tobias.

I tell Tobias while I am writing this that I have seen him being pretty crazy today, as I have a number of times earlier. He agrees. I tell him that I am describing it now and tell him what my conclusion is: that the craziness signifies that he is re-living the memory of dying.

His expression is seriously clear and not the least crazy. He says:

«Yes, that's right.»

He needs the toilet again. He has run to the toilet once an hour all day.

«You need the toilet, again?»

«Yes.»

«Yes, that's how it is when one dies, one urinates. That is what you are doing.»

«Yes.»

Tobias feels secure, now. His psychosis is not psychosis in the sense of being an escape from daily reality. His madness seems more like an attempt at reparation, if one can speak in terms of attempt and I think one can, taken in the context of my understanding of psychodynamic psychosis theory. The intention is to re-enact and reprocess those traumatic minutes when he died for a short while. When Tobias has taken his life situation to the limit of what he is capable of, then I have reason to believe that his existential self reaches down into the traumatic body-memory, deep within his subconscious.

This is not as fuzzy as some biological psychiatrists claim. There is sufficient evidence supporting the theory that the amygdale is the area that stores and sustains sensory input from life-threatening events. If these experiences are traumatic in the sense of being impossible to comprehend, understand and contain, then they will remain remote from conscious memory. The trauma will remain unprocessed and will not have been stored in the form of a narrative memory that can be remembered as «this is how it happened».[15]

Tore takes out a CD with classical music. He finds a very desolate and sad piece of music. Tobias lies with his head in my lap. He says: «Now». He is reliving his death now. His facial expression shifts between calm and torment. I tell him repeatedly to relax and relive his death without fear. I promise to rescue him. He survives. He says:

«Difficult. I can't tell the difference. Life and death.»

«No, you don't know the difference between life and death. It doesn't matter. You do know the difference between calm and fear.»

«Yes.»

Tobias sits up. Tore and I say that we experience the music as sad and desolate. Tobias listens. Tore says:

---

15 Unprocessed trauma memory is experienced as happening now, in the present. This is probably due to the fact that the memory is stored in the amygdala, which is a primitive survival-based memory- and feeling- depot. When an amygdala-based memory is activated, the body is put into a state of mind where the event is replayed using the senses that registered the trauma. Speaking and thinking about the event activates the hippocampus, and it is assumed that it is via this organ that the trauma becomes an experience and is remembered as being in the past. Both medications and psychotherapy have shown that the amygdala function is affected by treatment aimed at regulating anxiety and worry. In the current research, cognitive behaviour therapy was used, but there is every reason to believe that the same mechanism applies to any psychotherapy that relieves anxiety, regardless of the therapy's label. CBT was quite simply first out in arranging to be sponsored by the pharmaceutical industry. The psychodynamic movement was opposed to this, not least because of the desire to be independent of political and economic power structures. The journalist, Ingrid Carlberg, has described the market strategy behind the alliance between CBT, the pharmaceutical industry and research grants (Carlberg, 2008). Her source research is very thorough and enlightening.

«I can imagine that this music is mourning for a 23 year-old that has died in a bicycle accident.» Tobias reacts, moved.

«Oh!» he says.

«Yes, it is you,» I say.

«You died when you were 23 years old.»

«Oh,» he says and starts crying.

Tobias cries for five minutes, calmly and absolutely not crazily.

There are «brain-damage tears» that everyone who has heard and seen will recognize. It is crying that resembles that of a panic-struck infant. It is a crying out of which the individual cannot console himself. The person needs to be hugged. However, in the insane, epileptic, brain-damage pandemonium, the weeping person may not be able to trust anybody, and then the tears must be stopped and repressed. The crying turns to laughter or anger. Tobias' weeping this time is safe, and go the whole way. The tears resolve themselves into a quiet sadness and a peaceful calm. This is an enormous step forward. It is a step forward that is difficult to explain. It is not these kinds of events and developments that people have in mind when they ask how Tobias is getting on.

What happens next will show whether my hypothesis was correct or not. My hypothesis is that a person with traumatic brain injury gets in a state of confusion for a reason, namely, post-traumatic stress. An unresolved trauma that is extremely difficult to resolve owing to aphasia, owing to the phenomenology of the trauma memory as described above, and because of the limiting effects of the brain damage upon the ability to resolve, reflect and translate the trauma into a narrative memory.

The calm continues for a while. When his brain activity is at an intensively high level, Tobias has problems with his memory. On days like these, a neurologist would probably claim that a light epileptic activity is in progress all the time. In any case, this is what I believe. The one thing does not exclude the other. However, epileptic activity or not, the thoughts are not coincidental. They are individual expressions of a personal occupation with existential issues.

While we are sitting and eating, we talk about Tobias' fate. Tore expresses his admiration for Tobias' resilience and his suffering. As an example, Tore takes a rather simple feature of Tobias' disability – the paralyzed arm. With empathy and compassion, Tore describes how Tobias has created a positive life with the help of only one arm.

But Tobias isn't with him. He says:

«Now, good.»

He means that he can use his paralyzed arm now. We look at him in wonder. We ask him to show us what he means. We have a choice, here. We could keep straight faces and agree with him, that he can use his right arm. But, we don't want to encourage him in an illusion. We make an attempt to find a balance between respecting his view and the bitter truth. I ask Tobias to show us how he can use his arm. There is a spoon on the table. I suggest that he tests his right arm's usability. He agrees to this.

«Put your left arm behind your back, so that you won't be tempted to use it.»

Tobias follows this instruction.

«Would you now like to try to pick up the spoon with your right hand?»

It is so agonizing that it makes one want to cry, to stop him, hug him, and say that things are okay anyway. However, before this he must see the reality. He tenses his whole arm, his only way of contacting it. He battles, tries, twists his shoulder, his whole body, so that his arm moves over the table. He exerts himself so that his face turns red. His whole right hand clenches itself. He manages to touch the spoon with his clenched hand. He looks slightly triumphal, as if this proved him right, but it feels unworthy to let him deceive himself, like a small child.

I say:

«So close! Almost! Your right hand won't open. That is just where the damage in your brain sits; the brain can't get the hand to open itself. Now you can use your left hand to put the spoon into your right.»

Tobias does it. It looks as if he is going to give a victory cheer, but I repeat the word «almost» and Tobias sticks out his lower lip in a dejected, bitter grimace and sits down again.

Tore explains to Tobias that an arm is just an arm. Tobias would still be wonderful, even if the arm was amputated. I add that he is a genius of the one-handed-grip, that he has become left-handed and is extremely adroit; how many people can tie their shoes with only their left hand? He listens but his self-esteem is weak. He quickly returns to defence against insight, in a belief of being well and problem free.

«Can do everything, now ... Talk.»

«Do you mean that you are free from aphasia, now?»

«No aphasia.»

«You have no aphasia?»

«No, gone.»

«The aphasia is gone?»

«Yes, gone.»

«If you are free from aphasia then you can say your name and address without problems. You can say 'My name is ...', etcetera.»

Tobias:

«My name is ... (silence) ... my name is ... aphasia ... my name is ... Jonas. No ... my name is aphasia-Jonas ... my name is Jonas aphasia.»

I say:

«Tobias.»

«My name is Tobias.»

I say:

«Ka»
Tobias:
«Carolusson! My name is …»
I say:
«To»
«Tobias.»
«Ka»
«Carolusson! Yes. So!»

Tobias goes in to see TV. Star Wars is on stand-by and the text at the bottom reads: «We are searching through …»

Tobias reads aloud:
«We … we … see.»
I say:
«No. It won't be see. It will be s, ea, r ch, ing. Searching.»
Tobias:
«We searching … »

I read the rest of the text for him. I don't want him exposed to more frustration. I suggest a tablet before sleeping and he accepts this suggestion with pleasure, as if I had offered him a sweet. Maybe he thought it was what I meant, as I didn't use the word «pill» or «medicine», just tablet, as in a cough tablet. What he does get is a Nozinan, an anti-psychotic medicine that slows down thought-traffic and abnormally high brain activity.

Being the relative of a severely brain-damaged person does not get easier as time goes by. It does not become more manageable, as many people think. The process changes, however. We see new facets of Tobias. We see new possibilities. We loosen our grip on illusions. We mature and he matures. We accept his life-long disability. We dare to imagine a future for and together with a special son. In practical terms, we interact increasingly well together and find ways to seek and find the right levels of communication. However, our own feelings do not become calmer. The whole of the evening that I described above, I could feel how my pulse rose and my stomach was uneasy. I had a vague desire to flee. This is probably light anxiety, I told myself. I also thought; we need a holiday from this parent life. It is impossible just now, however. This will pass. Tobias will soon be harmonious and calm again, and Tore and I will forget this state, once again. We are now masters at enjoying these pauses from chaos. The pauses last much longer than the periods of crisis, in clock time.

While Tore and Tobias watch a film, I spend an hour on the computer with my mail, but I find it hard to concentrate on the contents of the letters, especially if they contain some kind of work task. One mail concerns the board of the hypnosis society and the treasurer is asking me if I can deal with a practical matter. It is quite a simple request, really. However, I simply cannot work out what it is that I am supposed to do. So, I ask the treasurer to deal with it himself as far as possible, and then tell me what remained to be done – but not today, on Wednesday at the earliest. I explain the situation in short, of course, but it is not in my character to avoid my duties within this society of which I am the president.

But, I can't trick myself, either. I am not in good shape.

«Aren't you going to go in therapy?» I ask my husband.

Tobias hears me, so I drop the subject. We concentrate on the film instead.

Maybe we ought to go, both of us? This is a shared suffering, if I may say so, deriving from our own beloved son.

THEORY

I summarize here the most up-to-date thinking about how and why trauma can be processed and healed with the help of therapeutic communication. As I wrote in «Reflections» in the chapter called «To realize or to avoid realizing», there is also research about how a person's experience of a situation can influence DNA activity. Ernest Rossi has collated

191

the results of contemporary neurological research. He finds the discovery that our genome can be influenced by psycho-social stimulation to be of especial interest. The greatest influence occurs in those moments of great strain, stress or panic. What we learn during these moments is state-bound. In other words, we store an emergency survival strategy for that charged instant. This state can last for up to two hours. If one has the opportunity to intervene and influence the ex-perience psychologically, calmly and trustingly, within this time frame, the development of PTSD (Post Traumatic Stress Syndrome) can often be avoided. In the case of no interven-tion, some form of PTSD can be expected. The most common symptom of PTSD is the return of the unprocessed experience of terror in the form of flashbacks. One relives a state of panic without realizing, in a number of cases, that it is an event that has already happened. One experiences it as happening right now. It can also turn up in dreams, so that one is awakened by the nightmare and feels the same as before; acutely and mortally threatened.

Since one finds oneself in the same state of mind as during the trauma, as can be seen by the levels of stress hormones during such moments, the experience can be influenced and processed, both psychologically and neurologically! (Rossi, 2003).

At the age of 70, Rossi had a stroke. He describes in an article how, in his dreams and in collaboration with his speech th-erapist, he could visualize his blood vessels, explore the da-mage and imagine a prognosis, a forecast and a strategy for an optimal rehabilitation (Rossi, 2005).

There is a study in Sweden concerning the fact that intensive care may have a traumatizing effect upon the patient, giving the typical symptoms of PTSD. Mona Ringdahl, RN, PhD., found that experiences of intensive care can produce anxiety and an inferior quality of life. One of four victims of an acci-dent that demanded intensive care had nightmares, hallucinations, and paranoid memories that the staff were trying to harm them (Ringdahl, 2008).

Is there anything one can do at the intensive care stage that will thwart the development of PTSD? Yes, there have been a number of articles on this subject. Firstly, I described in my previous book how I whispered calming suggestions into Tobias' ear while the intensive care nurses prepared the treatment that had to be carried out. The staff confirmed that I achieved a state of calm within Tobias that reached the deepest brain structures, beyond consciousness, since narcosis anaesthetizes the consciousness, but not those deeper structures that keep the patient alive (Carolusson, 2002).

In an academic research study by Katalin Varga and colleagues, the same question, the effect of communication and hypnotic suggestions on patients in Intensive care, has been examined. They relate that «coma loneliness» can cause trauma, and they describe how hypnotic communication strengthens the patient's experience of security and trust (Varga & Diószeghy, 2003).

If all this can be found inside, deep inside the patient's world of experience, then it is never too late to treat brain damaged patients with trauma therapy. Hypnosis is a good tool in this treatment. In an interesting clinical article about hypnotherapy of brain injured patients, Spellacy describes the advantages of hypnotic communication. Brain damaged people often have problems with attention and concentration; they often have aphasia, and memory loss. Simple words and a slow tempo are always used in hypnosis. One avoids complicated cognitive tasks and communicates on an emotional level. Therapists who use hypnosis in their practice are used to communicate with intense presence, focus, attention and empathy. The article describes three patients and Spellacy provides a good model to explain why brain-damaged patients respond favourably to hypnosis (Spellacy, 1992).

REFERENCES

Carlberg, Ingrid. (2008) *Pillret. En berättelse om depressioner och doktorer, forskare och Freud, människor och marknader.* Stockholm: Norstedts.

Carolusson, S. (2002) *Det finns någon därinne. Om vård, värde och värderingar vid förvärvad hjärnskada.* Lund: Studentlitteratur. Utgivarefr. 2010: Författaren. www.carolusson.se

Ringdal, Mona (2008) Memories and Health Related Quality of Life – in patients with trauma cared for in the Intensive Care Unit (Akademisk avhandling) Institute of Health and Care Sciences. Sahlgrenska Academy, Göteborgs Universitet. http://hdl.handle.net/2077/18650

Rossi, E (2003) Can we really talk to our genes? Psychosocial Genomics. *hypnos vol XXX, nr 1-2003.* ISSN 0282-5090

Rossi, E. (2005) The Memory Trace Reactivation and Reconstruction Theory of Therapeutic Hypnosis: The Creative Replaying of Gene Expression and Brain Plasticity in Stroke Rehabilitation. *hypnos nr 1-2005.* ISSN 0282-5090

Spellacy, F. (1992) Hypnotherapy following Traumatic Brain Injuries. *hypnos, vol XIX no 1-1992.* Welins Tryckeri Örebro. ISSN 0282-5090

Varga, K. & Diószeghy (2003) The use of hypnotic communication and hypnotic suggestions in the Intensive Care Unit. *Hypnos, vol XXX, nr 1-2003.* ISSN 0282-5090

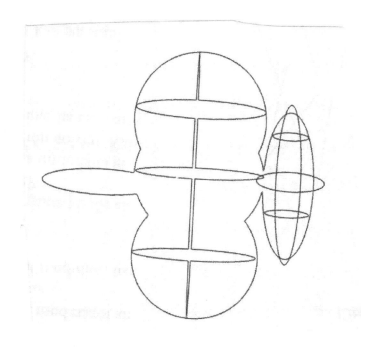

Drawing by Tobias

THERE'S SOMEONE IN THERE, ONCE AGAIN

It is a wonderful autumn day, one weekend towards the end of October 2008. I am going to rake up the leaves from the lawn. It has to be done, but it is a bit difficult for me since the wheel of my bike got stuck in a tram track and I have got a badly swollen bruise on my thigh, a torn shoulder muscle, and a sprained left thumb as a result. Still, best to keep myself active, I suppose. However, someone else who needs a good day is Tobias who is with us as usual during the weekend, and he has already been out for his walk. Tore is in town, so there is no-one to keep Tobias company indoors. The cat isn't that good at interpreting Tobias should he want to say something. Asking Tobias to help in the garden doesn't usually fall on fertile ground. Partly because walking about on a soft, uneven surface is difficult for him, he risks a sprained ankle, and also because he has difficulties understanding instructions. We've tried this before.

Let's try again! I give him a chance and ask him to put on his shoes and come out to me on the lawn in the garden. He comes and is in fact positive towards lending me a hand.

I give him the handy plastic rake and use the steel rake myself. I show him how to do it, and as readers who have used a rake will know, it is a question of pulling rather than pushing the leaves. We divide the lawn between us and I go to my part of it. When I look at Tobias I see that he is trying to push the rake in a forward manner. Once again, I tell him that it doesn't work like that; one must pull the leaves towards oneself, «like this …»

When I next look to see how he's getting on with his task, he is standing still, staring at the grass and the rake. He seems to be totally paralysed.

I consider the fact that he is in fact very badly brain-damaged. He probably can't understand this instruction, despite being in the best of moods and really aware. I watch him pushing the rake lightly forward.

Suddenly I have déjà vù. I remember how he was as a child. He's standing there testing whether it's possible to do it in the opposite way to what the adults say. Instructions are there to be tested and he wants to try his own way, stubbornly, just like the free spirit he is. Imagine if he succeeded! What a wonderful victory over mom's say-so!

As soon as I have got this image of my dear son's character, I laugh and tell Tobias how he has always wanted to go his own way, in the opposite direction. He laughs, too, with insight and charm, and his desire to rebel evaporates. Without further instructions or prompting, he does the job exactly as I showed him and within a few moments he has raked together three tidy piles of birch and oak leaves, effectively and adeptly, with the help of his left arm only. He is proud of his performance and I am endlessly thankful for Tobias' generosity in contributing to the housework.

There is someone in there, almost always in fact. Sometimes the inner driving force is anger, other times it is sadness, resignation and apathy, while at times it is quite simply the force of a creative, stubborn and wonderfully charming individualist. I must keep this in mind.

THE ROLE OF THE FAMILY MEMBER

Little brother Mårten and Tobias

I had a lecture yesterday for relatives that had been invited to hear me speak about when «life didn't turn out as one had expected» with lots of subheadings that appeal to those who know what it feels like when one's existence is turned upside down. Also for those who are trying to deny this feeling, because it hurts too much. More than one believes possible to experience.

I was nervous beforehand and wondered why. «Why am I nervous?» I asked myself.

I don't want to be nervous.

First, I am tempted to deny it. I don't want to be like that ... I don't want to be nervous ...

Then I did what is so popular these days; I coached myself. I told myself «You've done this so many times before, it'll be all right.»

Then I asked myself what every psychotherapist asks her patient: «What is the worst that can happen?»

«Well,» I replied, «I can stand there and realize that I am talking about things they don't want to listen to, or won't recognize within themselves.»

How do I cope with that?

This question caused me to realize that I just had to take that chance, and that it could really happen. I am only myself, I have my own experiences, and I can't promise that everyone in the audience will be pleased. This is the conclusion I drew. However, being a psychologist, I went deeper. I am an existential, dynamically-oriented person who believes in the power of feelings, so I took my nervousness and what my inner had to say about it, seriously. What did my state of stress want to tell me? There is an answer, as always when I make use of self-hypnosis, which is really simple to use for anyone used to introspection. I shut my eyes and send the question «what is this worry about?» down to my subconscious, a concept I use often with my clients as it indicates a depth. I relax and focus inwards.

The answer that surfaced is as follows: I felt that an audience composed of relatives to brain injured people is an impossible audience, if one wants to speak at levels that reach everyone. I felt deep inside something that I have learned from many seminars of the kind; this group is more heterogenic than other groups that have been called together because of certain common experiences. Yet, we were meeting together under just one heading: Family members.

When I entered the lecture hall, three people were already there. They had arrived nice and early. They had read my book «There's someone in there», and they started talking together, and with me, about their situations. They appeared to be exactly what they were: relatives full of feelings, engrossed in their own situation and thirsting for advice, support, and, most of all, hope that their future would be better than it was under the circumstances that they were battling with at the present.

The circumstances surrounding a person with cognitive difficulties, whether congenital or acquired, are varied. Brain damage manifests itself in such different ways that those affected are more different from each other than one might imagine. They have a variety of speech abilities, and mobility, different ways of thinking, varied access to emotions, different degrees of insight about their disabilities and need of assistance, different strategies for denial, for giving themselves a raison d'être, for taking space, for showing needs, etcetera. The differences are endless.

One parent was telling another about the communication tool, «Bliss», but the other parent already knew that her daughter did not have the required cognitive ability to make use of the symbols in Bliss. The well-meaning parent didn't get this hint and in all innocence continued to praise this tool with the strong commitment that parents usually have. One parent told me during the break that he had read half of my book but was finally forced to stop half way through – he had become painfully envious of the progress that my son had made, progress that his son was not making.

I wonder sometimes if there is something that is common for all us parents. I think there is. We parents, the ones that manage to stay, or find our way back to loving parenthood so that we, as much as time and energy allows, choose to be together with our child, we have something in common. We have an injured son or daughter.

In other family relations, when a brother, partner or parent is injured, I wonder whether the staying power is as strong or durable. As far as I know, many people with less binding roles choose to cut off the relationship or reduce the amount of time spent with the injured relative. This is why I will just speak about parents, now, those parents who have the will to continue fighting. Not all have this ability, and some steer clear of contact with their child in order to avoid the pain.

One does what one can, and I am not the right person to judge other people's choices.

We who choose to remain, we increase our input, and remain rooted in the early parent-child relationship that existed during the child's infancy. This is something that is almost impossible to understand. Without having been in the same situations you need a high level of empathy to figure out. Most people cannot understand.

I would like to warn about self-pity at this point. I do not want to encourage parents to be self-pitying. There is a masochistic martyrdom in self-pity that is not good for anyone, neither the person herself nor those around her, neither in the short- nor the long-term.

I mean it literally when I say that no-one can understand. I don't mean that others ought to be able to understand. We parents see and recognize the infant's helplessness. Our child has once again become dependent upon help. The same is true about parents to a child with congenital disability or oxygen deficiency at birth. These parents receive no natural help from life to separate from their child. If the child has a cognitive disability, the parents will continue to have an empathetic, listening role. It is not just that those around us don't really understand, it is even more complicated than that. In my experience, not only those around us but even those people that work professionally with disabled people react as if they are disturbed by the parents' proximity to their disabled young or adult child.

People with normal children and those who have no children at all tell us, more or less directly, and as if it was the most obvious thing in the world, that our child must be treated as if they had no disability in one specific issue, the importance of growing away from their parents.

Isn't that strange? Most people understand that a disabled person is in need of help and support in all sorts of ways, yet they cannot see that this need for help can be very naturally and very easily provided by the parents since this relation has a stable background based on the existence of this role since birth. There are exceptions in the cases where this caring relationship has not worked properly from early years and has not been repaired at a later stage. There can be many reasons why parents have been unable to give their child the necessary, reliable security and I do not want to place blame. There is also the situation where a child received a brain damage during her late teens and that the unfinished separation process of that age, is left permanently fixed in a distancing relation.

In these cases, the affected son or daughter can be caught up in the feeling that it is the parents in particular that they want to avoid being close to.

In the case where childhood was filled with empathy and love and the teenage revolt has been resolved into a more equal adult relationship, the early secure relationship will be a deep resource when life falls apart at the seams. The dependency of childhood will be a familiar safe house that will be reawakened at both a bodily and a mental, although subconscious level.

Writing this, I am uncertain whether I will be taken seriously by any other than those parents who have experienced the same thing. I risk a Catch 22 situation. Professional, non-relatives may mean that I am subjective and caught up in my own maternal role, and that I cannot see and understand what is best for myself and my son.

I choose to turn a blind eye to this kind of criticism. I have sufficient self-knowledge to know that I give my son as much freedom as he can manage, and encourage him to be away from me as much as possible, which he is five days a week, in fact. If I had been the kind of mother that felt a need to be needed, to compensate for a lack of meaning in life, I would never have travelled abroad for work reasons, with the latest trip lasting 10 days. Tobias gets upset when I am not within reaching distance. I test and test, time and again, to find out how much separation he can cope with. I do it for my own sake as I am longing for freedom. I probably also do it for Tobias' own sake, so that he can manage by himself, when he finally has to. I am not sure about this second reason, though. There are two theories concerning independence: the first is that we train and practice being independent until we finally cope. The second theory is that humans have an inner aspiration towards separation and independence, which awakens when dependence has been satisfactorily met, security has been internalized and one's self-esteem has been sufficiently confirmed. The latter view is found in psychodynamic, existential and humanistic psychology. But I must add that this psychology is only for normal development. Cognitive impairment in adult life is not normal. Academic psychology has no wider theory concerning the loss of cognitive abilities, from a deeper perspective.

Which is why I write this book.

Twelve years of involuntary, restricted parenthood has taught me and my husband that Tobias feels better meeting us regularly, preferably every weekend. It is as if he fuels his inner reserves of love in preparation for his weekly stay in his home, his daily activities, and his assisted adult world, that he tries to have and that he in fact copes with. He copes, with the help of lots of energy, a group of well-chosen assistants who have empathy, creativity and a humble respect for the unknown. Tobias strives to be on the same level as his assistants. He doesn't want to feel his dependence upon them, he doesn't want to be the underdog, and he does not want to be reminded of his «client» role. I have come to see that it is taxing for Tobias to constantly confront daily life that could have been filled with freedom and competence to make choices had he been able to live on, as he was when he was 23 years old. Thus, when he is with us, his parents, he can relax, accept help, rest his brain, and listen to instructions concerning shampooing and deodorant without feeling inferior.

This is what moms and dads do, it feels normal.

Any adult person with a dysfunction may feel some familiarity since childhood with being dependent on parental assistance, but it is also normal that one will protest against parental care. This is what usually happens during the teens plus a few more years. One says «no thanks» to one's parents' care and everything else in their behaviour that signals that they haven't yet realized that they should retreat. One protests before one is in fact competent to take on adult responsibilities and one keeps on protesting until the parents judge that one can manage adult responsibility and that it is time to drop the parental control and guidance function.

A cognitively disabled adult son or daughter will also protest sometimes, and do so as far as they are capable.

This was especially noticeable those few years after the accident when Tobias still felt himself to be the one he once was at 23 years old, and independent of us. This self image took ten years to change, after many stubborn reminders from our side about what had happened to him, what his brain damage implied and why life was different now. Sometimes he has relapses into a longing for independence. For instance, one morning when his assistant arrived, the flat was empty. The assistant went out to search. He met Tobias walking slowly and a little sadly. After a number of guesses and interpretations the assistant came to realize that Tobias had been longing to travel. He had gone down to the nearby ferry terminal for boats to Denmark. But he didn't know how to buy a ticket, so he had returned home.

When the protests and attempts at freedom have been unsuccessfully tested, as they are practically impossible, twelve years later, I can see that Tobias wants to and dares to relax in gratitude and an obvious desire for support, help, love and encouragement. He does all this like a child, sometimes. Can this be okay?

I say «yes», but not unconditionally. We also respect his integrity, and actively show that. We do it in the same manner as good parents respect their children's needs, feelings, and desires. In the same way that good parents allow their children to do those things they are capable of, and enjoy the fact that they can.

You can read more about this in the book *Your Competent Child* (Juul, 2011).

At the time of writing, I have managed to find some promising research about how psychotherapy can be used with patients with acquired brain damage. The author, Pamela Klonoff, has found that this group of patients needs to have a close family member in attendance, at least at the start of the therapy, and maybe the whole way through. She explains that, in good conditions, the patient can let the family member take on a role of being the auxiliary judgement that they themselves lack. Unlike other psychotherapy, where therapist and patient can enter into an alliance that helps the patient to detach herself from overly intrusive parents or partners, the family member is needed in the highest degree as participants in the psychotherapy process; as memory, support, sometimes as a mouthpiece and not least as being respected for their great value in the disabled person's life. Klonoff also emphasizes that the family are in need of psychological help themselves.

The commonest problems for family members is stress, confusion, insecurity, loneliness, neglect, abandonment and a lowered quality of life. Klonoff emphasizes the benefits of the same psychotherapist giving support to the entire family, especially just after the trauma (Klonoff, 2010).

Practice is always more complicated than theory. Research attempts to find general advice, as in the book mentioned above, but in practice, sensitivity to each family's unique situation, resources and needs is critical for knowing how to help best. My experience as supervisor and psychologist for this group of patients is that, eventually, the family is in need of relief. When a working network has been built up around a disabled person, in the form of personal assistants, support in the home, or staff in a daily activity centre then it is a relief for the family if these assistants can be spokespeople, memory and support in contact with health care. It may take many years to reach this point and it is necessary that the disabled person herself desires this and that she shows clearly that she trusts the assistants in question. The family must also have the insight that they will benefit and that the disabled person feels that this cooperation is a support. Mostly they do, even if the family itself is worried, stressed, and «difficult». It is as if the disabled persons would also like to be relieved of having to worry about the family and are happy that they receive good support. It is very possible that disabled people, deep inside, are more aware of the family's sorrow than they can express themselves.

There are no general principles for treatment that work for everybody. This is why staff supervision is important. This supervision is based on the unique situation and actual relationships.

REFERENCES

Juul, J. (2011) *Your Competent Child. Towards a new paradigm in parenting and education.* http://bookstore.balboapress.com

Klonoff, P. (2010) *Psychotherapy after Brain injury. Principles and techniques.* New York: The Guilford Press.

THE CAPACITY FOR GUILT AND REPARATION

We are in the kitchen. Tobias comes in with his empty coffee cup and puts it by the sink. I ask him to pour some water into the cup. The coffee has a tendency to stain the cup otherwise, though I say nothing about that. I perhaps should have, though.

Tobias cannot understand my instruction. He tries by putting his cup among the clean ones in the cupboard. Tore tries:

«Pour some water into the cup.»

Tobias is nonplussed.

Tore takes over, commenting that it would perhaps be better if Tobias got help from someone who doesn't irritate him at the moment. Tore means me. Tore asks Tobias if he knows how to get water. He knows and puts on the tap. They thus solve the problem.

In my defence, I point out to Tore that Tobias grip on words has been weak the last few days. Maybe Tobias has had a smaller epileptic fit at night, says Tore.

Since we are having a New Year dinner with some of our neighbours in the evening, I involve Tobias in laying the table. I wash six tin mugs and ask Tobias to give me the tea towel.

Just in case, I ask him in a neutral tone of voice:

«Do you know what tea towel means?»

«Yes,» answers Tobias in a self-assured tone of voice.

«Sure?»

«Yes!»

Tobias looks around. He looks at the dishcloth, and then searches the sink. After a moment, he takes an oven glove from its hook. He gives it to me.

«Is that a tea towel?»

«Yes.»

«Hmm, well it is made of cloth, and it is a kitchen thing. Not bad. On the same hook is this. It is perhaps this you meant, it's a tea towel.»

Tobias gives it to me.

«Thanks,» I say, with a smile.

I turn around and dry two mugs. I give the mugs to Tobias. He takes them with his left hand.

I turn back to the sink again.

Bang! A hard blow to my neck surprises me.

Tobias bends forward, and gets hold of his right hand with his left. He clenches both hands to his chest, as in a Tibetan greeting.

He bows his head and neck towards me in a deep bow.

Then he stays in that position.

A long time.

I ask him:

«Is this your way of saying sorry?»

«Yes.»

He stands still in this deep bow. Immobile.

I stroke his neck.

A minute goes by.

Tobias raises himself up and looks seriously at me.

I say:

«You are angry at your aphasia.»

«Yes.»

«You didn't want me to say that an oven glove is not the same as a tea towel. You just want it to be the same sort of thing, it is a kitchen thing of cloth after all, 'let me avoid being plagued by my aphasia'.

And I am cruel and say that there are different words for different things.»

Tobias:

«Yes. Difficult.»

«Difficult with aphasia?»

«Yes, very, very difficult.»

«Yes.»

«But not now, not now.»

I fear that he is on the way into denial of his aphasia, so I must balance on the very edge of empathetic attention to what he is capable of realizing and can cope with. I want to encourage and acknowledge insight:

«You admit to your aphasia now, which means that you can ask for help. That makes it easy to like you. No-one thinks that you are slow-witted just because you have difficulties with language.»

«Yes.»

«Well, yes, if they don't know you, you're right about that. If one doesn't know you one might think you are slow-witted. Those who know you know that you are intelligent. You just have difficulties expressing your intelligence.»

«Yes.»

«You have your imagery.»

The above conversation is an example of how difficult it is to harbour the loss of a cognitive tool, such as language, that needs to be expressed and thought in the form of words. Denial, like a protective blanket, is a constant attraction, letting one enter a world where one can do things that one, in fact, cannot. My choice is to pull him away from denial. If this is to succeed, I must try to give him both worth and dignity. This is difficult, and the risk that he gets hurt is a constant reality. It can lead to being hit, impulsively, as I described above. The wonder in it all is Tobias' ability to feel guilt about his deeds. He bowed humbly, not pretending, not strategically, neither entreating nor devastated. He expressed his guilt with dignity and generosity. How can I know this just through his simple act of bowing? It could be felt in the air. There was no doubt.

The process of development from primitive denial between good and evil, worthless and perfection, jealousy and generosity is a process that is described in great detail by Melanie Klein in her article *Love, Guilt and Reparation*. Klein's theory about guilt deeply explains the maturity that is in fact needed to leave denial and have the necessary sense of self to be able to feel the kind of guilt that awakens an inner desire to make amends. To be able to honestly ask for forgiveness is a sign of this kind of ability (Klein, 1993).

REFERENCE

Klein, M. (1977) *Love, guilt and reparation: and other works 1921-1945*. London: Dell Publication Co.

Dad and Tobias

LOVE AND DISABILITY

Tobias meets both in combination this year, 2009. We are thrown into both light and dark by turns. I will start with love.

We had almost given up hope that Tobias would find a woman. How does one find a woman when one cannot write (a personal ad), can't talk on the telephone (or answer when it rings), or go out dancing (not so easy when one has a bad limp and the right arm is stiffly affixed by one's side). There are meeting points on the internet for the disabled, but when Tobias has tried to make a date, the women have wanted to get to know him better on the internet site first. Which is something Tobias can't do. When I learnt more about this activity, I soon came to realize that many people there wanted the contact to remain as just an internet contact. Maybe they are afraid to make direct contact. Maybe they are afraid that they won't be accepted in a real meeting. Double bookkeeping. On the conscious level they long to be responded to by an attractive man. On a less conscious level they imagine that the disabilities can cause problems - «what if I'm not good enough?» In that case it is better to keep hoping, at a distance, without confronting a reality that could be painful.

The girl of the moment is Carola. Carola is perceptive. She knows that a man who functions normally will have a completely different tempo than herself. Her reading of the situation is not: «No normal man would like to spend time with me.» She dares to see things with much greater self-confidence. When she came to visit our family a couple of days during the summer in order to spend time with Tobias, she said to me, «I could never have a normal boyfriend. I would be far too stressed.»

211

It started like this: In March 2009, Carola once again looked at some newspaper clippings that she had been saving for two years. When she looked at the photo of Tobias and his younger brother, read the articles again, she recognized herself. She had read «There is someone in there», and was fascinated by Tobias' struggle, and had gathered up courage to get in touch. It took two years for that courage to grow strong enough for her to write a letter. Carola wrote a letter to Tobias, describing her own situation. She had also been 23 years old when her life changed dramatically. She had also lost friends, who had gone their own ways, building families and careers. Like Tobias, she was also dependent upon the support of parents and assistants. Carola wanted to break her isolation and wondered if Tobias would like to have some kind of contact with her, preferably by post or mail, as she was living in Hässleholm (230 km to the south of Göteborg). As Tobias can neither read nor write without assistance, we (the family) realised that mail/post contact would be frustrating for him and would peter out in the long run. How personal would it be when one is dependent upon having a spokesperson in both directions? Someone would have to read the personal letter from Carola aloud to Tobias. Furthermore, the process of guessing what Tobias wants to say in his letter and then having to read it up so that Tobias can approve it, would be even more complicated.

This sort of relationship would never feel genuine and real to Tobias. He has to meet eye to eye, mouth to ear, body against body, and scent to nose. Carola had chosen to write at just the right time. Without being aware of it, in her letter, she had managed to suggest days that coincided with a trip our family had planned to Denmark, to celebrate Tore's 60th birthday. As it was on our route, we suggested meeting for lunch in Lund, on the 1st of April. She agreed.

But, how was this going to work out? Tobias can't represent himself with words. He can only answer questions, and agree with or, by single words and body language, respond to other people's comments. We were to find that Carola had a severe hearing problem and her problems with mobility and her ability to grip demanded her total concentration while eating.

Anyway, Carola is sitting waiting for us in the restaurant foyer when we arrive. She's nervous; imagine if it's an April fool joke? Tobias telephone number is very similar to her own number, her Christian name is the beginning of his surname, and it is the 1st of April a day for playing tricks in Sweden. These are so strange coincidences that she had started to imagine that everything was some kind of elaborate joke. During lunch she is fully concentrated upon eating the fish soup she has ordered. In the pauses, she asks me about my book. Across the table, Tobias is sitting, silent. Across the table from me sits Carola, and beside her sits her mother, Gunnel. We two have great difficulty in finding our role in the proceedings. Mothers don't usually sit in on their adult children's' first date. However, Carola and Tobias need help – Carola with hearing, Tobias with talking.

Tobias is shy and unsure of himself. However, the only thing that is noticeable is that he makes no attempt to talk with Carola. I have to prompt him a bit to have the courage to toast her, which he finally does in an attentive, gallant manner. Then it is time for us to go our different ways. Carola seems surprised about this, she expected more time with Tobias. Well, Tore and I think as we continue the journey to Denmark. What kind of contact has this been? None at all?

We get the answer that same evening when Carola emails that she appreciated the lunch and writes that she would really like to see Tobias again. And she will. This is not so easy for someone with a disability. Carola has assistance until 16.00 after which it is expected that she will manage herself without any chance of going out or the pleasure that most of us have to cook something good if we so desire. She seems to have come to accept this, something that Tobias would never do. His assistants change shifts at 16.00 and stay until 22.00. However, now they both need time to plan and also to make sure that they have the money needed to be able to meet! Carola needs to check whether she can have assistance a whole day so that she can travel return Hässleholm – Göteborg. Tobias must make sure that his assistants can arrange their shifts and that his money is sufficient to pay for the assistant's ticket.

They manage to meet a few times up to July when we invite Carola to stay with us in our rented cottage on the Danish west coast for a few days. This is a big deal for her, and not only positive. New people, new situations, Tobias' brother's lively children, with the youngest, Tova, 1½ years old, jealously protective about Tobias ... Add to this having to call on a stranger (me) to help her find her way from the toilet in the dark of the night. This is, to put it mildly, bewildering to Carola.

Up until this time, Tobias has been rather stand-offish towards Carola. This is what his assistants have seen and Mårten agrees with them. They are concerned. She will soon lose interest if Tobias continues to be cool, bordering on arrogant, they think. Carola's assistant has also told Tobias' assistant that Carola is wondering whether Tobias really likes her.

What do we do? Well, we encourage Tobias to dare to show his inner feelings! He is in love, there is no doubt about that. He is so uncertain about her feelings, however, that he has been wary, not least for his own sake. So now we are encouraging him to have the courage to court her, show her he cares and to make this visit a memorable one for Carola. The result is a fantastic performance by Tobias: He is continually attentive to Carola's mood and with the help of tone of voice, touch and a readiness to support her physically and mentally, he is her constant companion, except for when he feels that they need a little time apart. They share a room at night and Tobias continues his courting in the hope of even better things to come.

The next morning, Tobias tries to explain something to me but can't manage to get his meaning across. Carola takes over and explains: During the night they had agreed to just remain friends for the moment, to wait to see how their relationship developed over a longer period. Now they are just friends. Tobias concurs: Yes, they both agree about this.

Two days pass. They hug and kiss, and Tobias is intensively thoughtful in a way that I haven't realised he is capable of. And, Carola becomes afraid of all this. Her life has been quiet, and peaceful, at home with her parents or with assistants, a few trips abroad to her brother or to an old friend. No love affairs, no flirting or intimacy for the last fifteen years. Her body has changed; it doesn't obey her and doesn't look like the one that was her at 23 when she was in the mix. Just how sexy does one feel then? This is my interpretation of why Carola feels a resistance to the intimacy that Tobias offers.

He is of the opinion that she is very sexy and attractive.

On the way home from Denmark, Tobias has a manic, psychotic episode, probably as a result of too little sleep and a frustrated longing for confirmed love. His behaviour is dominated by fantasies about having total control over the entrances and exits of the boat, a refusal to make use of the lift, and other symptoms of brain collapse. I shall describe this in the next chapter as an illustration of the connection between frustration, self-doubt and psychosis.

In this chapter I will confine myself to love and disability.

When we finally arrive home, after a number of incidents, it becomes clear just how frustrated Tobias feels. I help him to write an email to Carola. He needs to know whether there is hope of an intimate relationship in the future or whether she only desires a platonic relationship. He needs to know now whether it is only friendship that she wants. If this is the case then Tobias will need support of the family and assistants to stop hoping for something more. However, if she feels something stronger than friendship, as her kissing seemed to indicate to Tobias, then he is prepared to wait with intimacy, as she is worth waiting for.

Her answer gives reason for hope. She feels a strong security in Tobias' arms and she is longing for those arms. So when they meet again, Tobias behaves as he had during the spring and neither his brother nor his assistants try to deter him from deciding the level of intimacy with Carola that he feels is right. The result is that Carola gets the message that Tobias is prepared to wait. He is not in the least intrusive, rather the opposite! She is allowed space within which she can yearn. And she does. Very soon an email arrives telling Tobias her answer, which is that her feelings are warm and sometimes red hot.

He is calmer now, as she has responded to his offers, as far as we can judge. Right now they are a pair. How they are when intimate, I do not know. I am wondering about asking Carola, woman to woman, whether they might have use of counselling, externally. I presume that she does not want advice from her mother or me. Though how can I know? Tobias might possibly get advice from his brother, though perhaps more likely from a neutral, professional counsellor? Maybe they can manage this between themselves in their own way – I just don't know!

I shall not tell any more in a book about how this private matter develops and what answers Tobias and Carola have come up with, but the subject is of great interest for many disabled people.

When the brain has been damaged and the family and assistants must act as spokespeople, it is not easy to know when it is time to offer help in such personal subjects as sexuality and intimate acts. Pride in being able to manage this oneself collides with difficulties in knowing one's own body, or being able to concentrate on one's partner's body. People with aphasia and difficulties in using parts of their body, such as the hand, arm, speech and hearing, how do they manage?

There are many questions, but of greatest importance is that disabled people with brain damage get help to realise that seeking help or advice is a possibility. They need help to see that this is not a weakness. One can perhaps relay the attitude that this is more a desire to develop and deepen their love!

This must be an important subject for many disabled people. The question was actualised in the 1970s by Gunnel Enby, a disabled author from Göteborg, who became famous for her fight for the sexual rights of disabled people. It would seem as if this debate has ebbed out. The 80's was the decade for the strong. Growth, luxury, stock market investments, yuppies, idiotic arrogance, and the gullibility of the masses ruled, leading to the financial bubble bursting in the beginning of the 90's. Sweden came to its senses, people became a little more humble and the disability movement managed to row ashore a project to force the government and parliament to pass a new law giving the disabled the right to live like the non-disabled: LSS - the law on support and services for certain disabled people, which came into force in 1994. During the 90's the economy got back on its feet, or rather the economists fixed the statistics, the dollar was tweaked. On the 20th March 2003, USA started its war in Iraq, Western bankers, especially in USA, loaned more to households and blew a little more air into the bubble that finally burst, first «over there», spreading later like rings on water to the rest of the world, culminating in the crash in 2007. I am no economist, but my husband, Tore, has engrossed himself in national economy and politics in order to try to save the fond that he had built up for Tobias, from being dragged down by the crash that he predicted. The crash came and the investments shrank to nothing, despite Tore's precautions. He is back again, he believes in his investments. I believe in nothing, just income from hard work. I know nothing else. I hope I'm wrong and he's right.

In the wake of the economic crises, we can see a depletion of resources throughout Europe. The personal assistance that we in Sweden are so proud of has become increasingly difficult to obtain by those that really need it. The Swedish Social Insurance Agency is cutting back on all forms of financial support, LSS is toothless, and relatives to the disabled are bending under the burden. At the same time, we relatives are so important – a Council employee can hardly give the love necessary for a meaningful life. This can only be found in one's own family, with very close friends and with a loving partner, if you are lucky enough to meet a partner. Sometimes, assistants can also be so close friends that a kind of loving contact arises. I recognise this from my work as a psychotherapist. Psychotherapists and assistants have something in common in this respect even though their professional roles are very different. The similarity lies in the fact that assistants have to «go deep» in their attempts to feel and understand the state of feelings of their client in order to work in the best possible way. To be seen, understood, and confirmed in this manner, with imaginative empathy in other words, is of immense importance for patients in psychotherapy and for users of personal assistance. It also arouses many questions concerning the nature of being «professional». How much psychological and physical intimacy can one offer? When is it better to keep at a distance and in that case «how»? My answer is that it varies. The assessment will be the result of finding a balance between respect, integrity, concern and care. How can one evaluate this? Can one be inconsequent and adjust treatment to the specific situation? I answer – yes. Courage is necessary, though, when being personally explicit as to the reasons for the variations that occur when one is professionally flexible. One learns from every new situation and a tacit, communicative competence will eventually develop.

An excellent way of becoming competent is to read biographies and case-studies, as well as reflecting about occurrences at work. Every single example that one studies in detail will give insight, leading to a better handling of similar situations at a later date. The key arena for the type of reflection that promotes such skills is process-oriented tutoring, which means that the same supervising consultant will follow the staff's development over a longer period of time. Supervision is one of the best instruments to ensure quality.

Tobias and Carola

IN LOVE BUT FEELING UNWANTED

I have never seen Tobias so thoughtful and loving, so quick to respond and so willing to court as during those three days that Carola visited us in the rented cottage in Denmark, one week in July 2009.

Tobias had an epileptic seizure the night after she had travelled home. The following day he was calm and gentle. We were to leave for home the very next day and this is when the reaction came. It had all been too much. He had behaved really well, he had been so empathic and attentive but at the same time he longed for his love to be reciprocated. He had been hoping for a night of love. He had been looking forward to this and hadn't anticipated being rejected. And when he

Tobias and Carola in Denmark

was rejected, he was in total agreement with Carola. They both wanted to take things easy, to be just friends and await developments. Or rather, it was more a question of Tobias smoothly adapting to Carola's wishes.

It is time to travel home. While we are waiting to drive onto the ferry, Tobias gets impatient and opens the car-door in order to walk onto the boat. To our relief, Tobias directly accepts Tore's information that one is not allowed to enter the boat via the car-deck. After a while, Tobias needs to go to the toilet and his patience is tried again since we tell him that we cannot take the car onto the ferry without all the passengers inside and we cannot hinder all the cars behind us from driving on when our turn comes.

We have reported disability-needs and there is a place reserved for our car close to the lift. Tobias isn't so disabled that he can't walk, so I sometimes feel that it is cheating to make use of facilities for the disabled just in order to get a better place. However, in situations like this, it is necessary to avoid everything that can provoke Tobias to take a short-cut, get stressed or want to go off in the wrong direction.

Tore and I decide that I will go straight to the restaurant and get a table so that Tobias doesn't have to stand in a queue. Tore goes with Tobias to the toilet. He refuses to take the lift and goes up the stairs with Tore in his wake. Today, Tore has painful knees and I see that he ought to have used the lift. He uses his arms to help pull himself up after Tobias. Up on level 7 we find a toilet. Tobias is in an oppositional mood and refuses to go into the men's room with Tore. Tore goes in himself. It is at this point that a misunderstanding, which I imagine most parents are familiar with, takes place. Yes, even parents to small children and also the middle-aged sons and daughters of senile parents. Senile people rarely get the opportunity to travel by the ferry, though. Unfortunately.

The misunderstanding? I manage to persuade Tobias to go into the men's room. I believe that Tore has understood this and would be waiting for Tobias inside. Therefore, I rush off to level 9 where we have a table reserved for the whole family of seven; grandchildren included. My idea is to avoid queuing with Tobias. It takes me a while to find the right restaurant, and when I find it, Tore is standing there. Alone. Tore gets upset – how could he know that Tobias had gone into the toilet? However, we are used to acting constructively and we make a quick decision. Tore goes down two levels again, to see if Tobias is still in the toilet.

Finally, we are all sitting together in the restaurant and we have control over the situation for a few hours. When we are in a more confined space, we aren't concerned at all. Tobias has never shown any signs of being suicidal, and he has never lost his commonsense to such a degree that he can't judge heights or feel tempted to jump off the boat to take a dip in the sea. If he should decide to wander away, then one just has to follow to see what he gets up to and maybe apologise on his behalf to strangers whom he either treats as his closest friends or his worst enemies.

When it is time for us to go down to the car deck, Tore goes towards the middle of the boat as the lifts are located there. I realise that Tobias has no intention of coming with us this way. He has a much better idea. He has gone towards the fore of the boat and has met a queue of people there in front of the next set of stairways. I get Tobias to come with me to the middle of the boat on the excuse that we will avoid the crowds that way. This proves to be wrong as after a long wait and masses of worry that Tobias will seek out other ways down, the lift doors open – and the lift is full of pushchairs and families. There is room for us but Tobias declines to get in. After another patient wait, the lift comes again, still full of people, but I manage to convince a reluctant Tobias that it is okay for us to get in.

We are using a hired car and in the luggage boot we have stuff that must be brought to our office in town. We decide that Tobias and I shall make our way to Brännö by the first boat and that Tore is to take a later boat after returning the rental and the baggage. We miss the 18.35 boat by one minute, which means that we have a 55 minute wait for the next boat. I will have to keep Tobias calm and under control for 55 minutes! Not easy as events proved.

I have a beer crate on a yellow trolley and two heavy bags of food that I have to put down in order to sit with Tobias on a bench. Luckily we have few thieves at Saltholmen.

We sit on the bench. Just like in Denmark, this will be a long wait and I am prepared for an impatient Tobias. A boat is moored to the quay. It says «Saltholmen» on its destination sign. The deck man and hands are making the boat shipshape, pulling up the gangway, shutting gates in the fore, anchoring properly with the rope over the fore, connecting an electric cable, etcetera. Two cleaners are busy cleaning.

Suddenly, Tobias gets up and tries to go onboard. My attempts to stop him with gentle informative words have no effect whatsoever. He climbs over the rope, opens the gate and steps onboard. The deckhand looks questioningly at him and asks «where are you going?» Tobias points self-assuredly into the boat. The deckhand says «This boat is going nowhere this evening. We have closed down for the night.» Tobias takes a couple of steps back, but quickly changes his mind when he realises that he is being amenable. He knows best when he is in this mood. So he says «no». I hope I can solve this situation without any trouble. Tobias has never hit an unknown person while psychotic, but I am always afraid that it will happen one day. I inform the deckhand, in a voice that I hope will tell him that he is dealing with an unbalanced person just now, and that Tobias thinks the boat is bound for Brännö.

The deckhand, who is young and wants to finish his shift, becomes irritated and mutters «I haven't time with this sort of thing», and just to be on the safe side I say «Take it easy, he can be difficult in this mood,» and the deckhand gets on with his work. I say something, I can't remember what, and Tobias comes off the boat with me. We sit back on the bench and in order to keep him with me I open a conversation: «It was a good thing we got off the boat; it seems as if the deckhand has lots to do getting the boat ready for the night.» Tobias almost gets angry. «Ohh???» he says, doubtfully. I say, «Yes, it was good he told us we were on the wrong boat.» Tobias is repentant and wants to say sorry and thanks. He finds the word «thanks» and calls it out to the deckhand who is busy with the electrical cabinet on the quay. When there is no response, Tobias repeats his «thanks» a little more loudly. I am worried that Tobias will go over to the man, and be tempted to board the boat again. It is that kind of insistent thanks that one finds with people who are drunk or on drugs and who are easily irritated. You meet them on the tram, or in town, putting out a hand and demanding eternal friendship. It is a very special mood that gives you the feeling that the person saying thanks is trying to get the upper hand in his desire for attention. So I get up and go over to the deckhand and tell him that Tobias feels apologetic and wants to thank him. The deckhand turns to Tobias with a smile and says «Okay». Things are back to normal again, and Tobias has forgotten all about it, so he can start from the beginning again. Once again, he thinks this boat is bound for Brännö. So, he climbs onboard. The deckhand ignores him this time but one of the cleaners stands at the entrance with his arms outspread. I repeat it all again - that Tobias thinks this boat is going to Brännö. The young man says that this isn't correct, and Tobias says «isn't it?» and turns back. We get off the boat, but after a few minutes he is back in a state of omnipotence, in which he knows better than everyone else in the world. He steps onto the boat for a third time. This time I am afraid. Not about what Tobias might get up to, but about whether the guys on the boat will lose patience and a provocative threat-scenario develops. During all the psychotic incidents that Tobias has been involved in, we have always managed to avoid unpleasant confrontations with strangers. I do not know whether this has been by skill or because Tobias has a mental barrier for destructive behaviour towards strangers.

Tobias walks over the foredeck and into the passenger cabin. The cleaner is a little perplexed and the deckhand just gets on with his job. Now, the captain has appeared, on his way to a small office. He is about 45 years old and seems calm and competent. I feel that he understands my plea when I tell him that Tobias thinks that the boat is going to Brännö. The captain looks at Tobias and says: «Oh no, it's not this boat, the boat that goes to Brännö is Skarven». In actual fact the boat going to Brännö isn't «Skarven», it's «Fröja» but that doesn't matter right now. The captain has taken the name of any one of the boats by chance as he feels he needs to say more than just «No». By avoiding the emphasis on impediments, and highlighting possibilities the captain demonstrates good psychological competence. This is the right way to treat a manic person. He avoids sounding too authoritative and suggests an alternative in accordance with Tobias' own idea.

He accompanies us back to the gate and shows Tobias the best way to step over the rope. Perhaps he has seen Tobias before on the boat and knows that he has a physical weakness on his right side.

How do I now avoid a repetition of the boat ritual? I say to Tobias encouragingly: «Let's go and look for the Brännö boat!» I know that the boat hasn't arrived yet, but I must keep Tobias occupied. So I read the signs saying: «Not this boat» and «here it says 'Bicycles can be taken onboard' ...» I take the opportunity to ask Tobias if he would like a Nozinan that would calm his thoughts a little. He has already taken two 10mg diazepam today, one this morning before leaving the house in Denmark at 11.30 and one onboard the ferry at 16.00, which is 20mg diazepam in other words. The effect is that Tobias had become wobbly and forgot his habit of turning his head to the right in order to compensate for his part blindness, with the result that he knocked into posts and people on the ferry. However, the diazepam didn't affect his restlessness, willpower, anger and intensity in the least. This is why I now offer him this anti-psychotic medicine. He agrees. Good. Tobias takes a tablet and I know that it takes at least one to two hours for the effect to work. After a few minutes, the Brännö boat arrives. Tobias climbs quickly onboard and I carry my bags of food and crate of beer from Denmark onto the boat. No time to relax, though, as Tobias seemingly has to demonstrate his individuality once again. The stairway to the upper deck is barred with a yellow-black chain. Tobias knows what that means. Despite this, he climbs over the barrier and goes up to the upper deck. I look up carefully to see whether he stays inside or goes out onto the open deck. He has sat down close to the stairway, so I decide to not go up after him. I imagine that his behaviour is not so innocent, but more a way of provoking me. I am right, it is no fun up there, and he soon comes down and sits near me, two seats away, though.

We have a calm conversation on the boat and when we get off at Brännö, Tore's cousin, Cecilia, is standing there. She is renting a cottage on Brännö and is on her way to town. Not knowing Tobias' state, she stretches out her arms for a hug and Tobias behaves normally, gives her a hug, and they stand talking for a while. When she then goes onboard and she can't see him, Tobias scowls angrily. We get onto Brännö's taxi-bus and Tobias behaves himself during the ride.

The most obvious symptom of craziness that evening is his tendency towards anger. It comes in waves. He will give a scowl and then growl a bit. However, he doesn't act out his anger. I manage to see his anger when it is coming and, to my joy, he can accept my reading: «Is there a wave of anger coming now?» He laughs and says «Yes. Grrrr!»

At seven o'clock that evening it is time for another Nozinan if we are to have a quiet night. Tobias falls asleep and awakens at eleven Sunday morning. His eyelids are swollen as they often are after taking anti-psychotic medicine. Sunday is free from medicine and filled with talks about Carola, sex, his enormous focus on courting, being loving and his unfulfilled hopes of a night of love, while maintaining his attitude of waiting, having patience, and hoping that his dreams will be fulfilled eventually. He is in love, he is disappointed, but he wants to show consideration. These talks go right in. During the talks he is collected and clear-headed.

When he gets no help to talk about these things that have influenced him so emotionally, he retreats from himself in order to lessen the pain. He is «100%», he says. I, on the other hand, am «0%». Tore is «100%». The two of them are perfect whilst I am useless. I see this as being about me as a woman, like Carola, and women have the power to reject and frustrate him. Tobias assumes the power to reject, so that it is I that am rejected. Tobias agrees with my interpretation that it is a question of all or nothing; valuable and totally perfect or worthless and useless. I try to make a confrontational interpretation.

«You mean that you are quite perfect and do everything right and always know everything. Yet, yesterday you got on the wrong boat. How do you explain that?»

«Yeah, how explain that ...?» says Tobias, thoughtfully, and is silent for a while.

I steer our dialogue back onto the subject of feelings. Which feelings are important right now? I guess and get agreement with joy, sadness, anger and disappointment. «Absolutely!» says Tobias about the word disappointment. We decide that disappointment is the strongest emotion. He is disappointed about everything about life, but not Carola. This is probably true. He is in love, he respects her drawing up lines of conduct and he is disappointed about his life situation. Perhaps he feels deep inside that had he not been injured, then he would have been able to seduce anybody he wanted, whenever he wanted. As far as I know, this is how he was during his late teens.

Tobias says «five». I can't understand what he means so I give him some pen and paper. He draws the palm of a hand, then another hand and two feet, followed by the owner's face above/between the hands, a smiling face, a nose, two eyes and two angry eyebrows. He asks: «angry?» I look and say: «angry eyebrows and a smiling mouth». This contradiction worries Tobias. I wonder whether this contradiction is within him, so I say: «angry and happy». I associate it to his agreement about his disappointment, so I say: «and maybe disappointment is at the root?» «Yes,» says Tobias and shows me that disappointment can be found at the back of his head. Tore comes in and sees the drawing. He gives us his interpretation: «The hands are maybe Carola's hands, when she shuns you. Go away! say the hands.» Tore says this in a childish, cute sort of way. This expression is a family expression, namely. It is from Mårten's obstinate period as a three year-old. He always angrily screamed «Go away!» when he was at odds with the world and himself. I think that Tore's interpretation sounds reasonable but Tobias says no, probably because he doesn't want to give Tore his due, or because he wants to maintain his positive feelings for Carola and hope that everything works out as he wants it in the end. I think that he has drawn Carola's rebuffing eyebrows and inviting smile since he experienced her as being inconsistent by accepting his kisses but rejecting him in bed. Women are often like this, even certain men, but everything is straightforward for Tobias, and this play, this shyness, maybe inhibitions, maybe signs that Carola is not yet in love with him – this he cannot understand.

I go to the bathroom. When I return Tobias seems really nice so I give him a smile. His soft eyes harden directly and I smile again and say in a childish tone: «Go away!» while holding out my hands like in his drawing. Tobias laughs warmly. I ask him: «Was this how you felt? Don't just stand there looking cute! Go away, I'm big now!»

«Big?» says Tobias humbly and smiles back.

Tore is frying mincemeat in the kitchen. He asks us if we would like a little bacon in the meat sauce. I say yes, while Tobias says that it is so-so, and he demands in that case «100%» if he is going to eat it. I add that he sometimes eats food that is 80%, not quite perfect in other words. Tobias starts talking about percentages as mathematical terms. We compare percentage with per mille and Tobias agrees with me that 100% is equal to 1000 per mille. He adds that 1% is more than 1 per mille. We chat a while about maths being his best subject at school.

Tobias then says: «Am big now.» I ask if he means that he is 36 years old. He agrees and then adds the word «five» returning to his picture with the five fingers of the hands. He wants to draw something. He points down the middle of the paper. I ask him if he means the navel. He says «under the navel» and I interpret this as the genitals. He says yes. I ask him to draw what he means. He draws a penis, looks at me and asks: «you?» I say that I don't have a penis. Tobias then says, to my surprise: «No, clitoris». He then draws the female genitals alongside the penis. I didn't know that he has this vocabulary. He has lost so many words due to his aphasia. This word, however, has probably been very much alive this last week. His psychosis becomes much more understandable as a crash following crushed expectations.

We then start talking about Tobias' longing for sex. I ask him to explain just where Carola put in the veto. Not out of curiosity, but to help him deal with his frustration, but he can't go that far. Instead, he says: «we banged like hell». Yet, as both Carola and he had told me that they had decided to postpone sex, I say to him that this is just wishful thinking, and Tobias accepts this directly. He agrees that he would like to have gone further but he wanted to take Carola's limits into account. He is sad that Carola didn't want to go that far and he wonders why. I try a guess: «shy, or afraid that she isn't good enough?», «unaccustomed?», but truth to tell, I have no idea what she feels. Perhaps she doesn't know herself.

It was not before I put this in writing that I realise that we have just illustrated his drawing. I invite with smiling lips, Tobias takes a rebuffed stance with angry eyes and I lighten the mood with played anger that is based on sound and well-known family history.

In the evening, Calle, Tobias' assistant, phones to hear how things are. Tobias appreciates the fact that Calle cares. Tobias decides to go to bed at 22.00 and he sleeps without medicine. Waves of anger come the next day, mostly concerning matters that are usually just routines. He refuses to use shampoo. I can see that this refusal is an idée fixe, a mental state in a tough situation. This is why I just stand outside the shower cabinet and wait. After a few minutes, things clear, Tobias says «okay» and realises that shampoo is acceptable. After this, we have a normal 30 minutes followed by more anger but in the form of a need for solitude. He goes up to his room and slams the door. When he comes back again, he has changed clothing. He wants coffee. He gets a cup that he sips, then gets up, leaving the coffee and goes to the TV. He is calm again for about half an hour. He then goes off to do something, but doesn't seem to know what. We suggest that he goes and lies down for a while.

THE ABYSS

Towards the end of 2009, I had a dream. Why should I describe a dream here? It is because this dream was a great source of knowledge. This is what I believe. Sometimes, dreams can be an intensively concentrated source of information. Dreams work like this: When we ask questions that are not just about facts, but involve feelings as well, questions that can hardly be answered by a dictionary or an encyclopaedia. These questions tends to remain in our subconscious until such time as our collected bank of feelings and events come together to give us an answer. These answers often turn up in the form of «Aha-feelings» or in a dream. I often awake after this kind of dream. These are dreams that create order out of chaos. The function is a problem-solving. I distinguish it from wishful dreaming. Wishful dreaming consists of dreams that are about well-being, desire, pleasure, rest, or a successful achievement. Problem-solving dreams give us answers that lie at such a deep subconscious level that our consciousness can't quite grasp them in when awake.

The so-called day residuals that I believe was the source of my dream is as follows: Tobias, Calle (personal assistant) and I attended a lecture yesterday. A social worker talked about her book on the topic of LSS. The lecture was organized by an association called (free translation) Brain Power. We were a small group, three mothers, one father, one participant who I believe has an acquired brain injury, one member of the board, and Tobias and his assistant, Calle.

An upcoming lecture with the heading «Letting go» was mentioned. The mothers sighed. How is one supposed to let go? «I've tried,» said one of them, «but nothing happens.

My son gets nothing from the Community if I let go». She explained that relatives have to fight hard for the rights of the disabled, and, as a relative and/or trustee, one is expected to be the spokesperson. I said: «Yes, I think I know how let go as much as is realistically possible». I asked Tobias if he agreed. «Yes,» he said, though I wasn't certain that he understood what I had meant. I have the habit of keeping every event that evokes my urge to understand, in the back of my mind, so I probably brought this uncertainty into my dreams that night. I don't want to have unconscious motives for not letting go. I want to be aware of the boundaries between my own and Tobias' needs of having me available.

I dream that we are leaving the lecture. We are in a wide space that I have never seen before. We are abroad, in a simple, underprivileged country with empty, half-built buildings, sand and concrete. We are perhaps in Cuba, or Rumania. I have a feeling that the country is «primitive» in a neutral meaning of the word. Neither undeveloped, nor uncivilized, just on the way from something to something else at an undemanding, slow rate. The ground is full of muddy pools. Suddenly, Tobias steps in a pool and sinks down into it. I expect that he will only sink a little bit, and manage to get out again. Then I see him sink further, so quickly that I haven't time to go and help him. I lean over the hole, look down and see that he is standing down there, on a slippery, muddy and wet little hill that is quickly collapsing.

There are deep twisting tunnels into which he is slipping, far from hope of being rescued. I can feel his horror, a totally unbearable horror at the total hopelessness of sinking deeper while seeing me up there in the opening, in the light. I say to a man beside me, probably a personal assistant: «We must phone 112!» I get out my mobile phone and punch in 112, realizing that Tobias is drowning down there. I get a recorded message in my ear and it is obvious that no one can help us now. I can see two scenarios: that Tobias manages to get a foothold somewhere down there in the deep so that he can start to walk until he finds help somewhere, hopefully before he dies of exhaustion. He is seldom afraid as long as he can keep his feet, I have time to think. The other alternative also makes itself known. «Perhaps he will die now, and we can stop worrying about Tobias.» However, the worst with this dream is the horror that I experience as Tobias' horror, a horror that I can't defend myself against! I am not going to have peace of mind if he dies; I am going to be tortured by his terrible, last moments of life. Just sinking deeper and deeper watching his mother disappear up there, having to give up without comfort, without warmth …

Then I wake up.

A dream like this is better than any textbook on psychoanalysis in the world when it comes to insight into the horror of helplessness. When I had analysed my dream I came to realize that it was about helplessness. Tobias' helplessness, not mine. I had asked whether I ought to let go more than I do. I had asked the self-critical question of whether I keep contact with Tobias more than he needs and more for my sake than his. My conscious answer was no. My dreamed answer was also no. Anyone who doesn't know me might imagine that the dream might reflect my anguish about letting go of Tobias, an unrealistic fantasy that he will die if I'm not there all the time. Against this interpretation is the fact that I am always happy when Tobias books in meetings with friends on a Friday, Saturday or Sunday, when he is usually with us parents. I don't allow myself to worry when he sleeps alone in his flat, despite the fact that he can have extremely severe epileptic fits when he sleeps. I can really enjoy travelling without Tobias. I can also deeply like it when he travels somewhere and the more he can get help from others, the freer and happier I am. It is then that I can enjoy a little of that freedom that middle-aged people with adult children usually have. To be on the safe side, I occasionally ask Tobias if I'm being too mothering, and get in touch too frequently. His answer is a resounding no.

That he is happy every time he sees me or hears my voice is beyond question. When I am away somewhere, he is usually worried, restless and sometimes psychotic.

I understand the nature of psychosis in accordance with psychodynamic knowledge about splitting mechanisms, denial of weakness and vulnerability as well as pure terror. My dream made this picture much more vivid. I am needed as a platform to stand upon. This was the answer to my unconscious question: Am I honest when I say that I have let go as much as I possibly can? Yes, because if I let go any more than I already have, then Tobias will sink. I can wish that things were different, but he needs me.

The dream helped me understand how he feels just before the symptoms of psychosis take over and save him from impotence, if no one is there at the time to hold him. I am the person who can best find the words to describe what he feels and who can interpret his vulnerability when he is in crisis. He sometimes has flashbacks in which he relives how the blood flowed out of him, his breathing ceased and life went out. My dream is perhaps how life-loving Tobias experiences things since 1996 and through all the subsequent flashbacks. He is in trouble every time he loses his grip on reality. Everyday life contains so much that can remind one that death can come in a blink of the eye and trust in life can disintegrate. I will not let go, Tobias.

I will be there in your vicinity as long as I live. Ready to keep you here. I will take a break sometimes, travel and get on with my work and my interests. You manage things better and better.

I also know that you are secure with your assistants and teachers in your daily life, so long as there is no crisis. Then I can keep in the background, in my own foreground, in my own perfectly wonderful life and allow myself to forget you a while. But I am always ready.

HOW ARE YOU THIS SPRING?

- I ask Tobias on the first day of May 2010. He's sitting in a chair at my bedside. We're eating some salad and drinking the tomato juice that Tore has served us. I'm in bed with a sore throat and fever.

«Fine, lovely.»

«Are you longing for a girlfriend these days?»

«Yes. A bit.»

«Is there anyone interesting at Grunden?»

«Don't know … But. Better and better.»

«You mean you're getting better and better … so that you can meet a girl?»

«Yes.»

«Are you aware of what your difficulties are?»

«Er … yes.»

«What?»

Tobias points at the damaged part of his brain.

«The injury?»

«Yes.»

«Anything particular about the injury?»

«M …»

He can't explain.

«You are aware of your injury?»

«Yes.»

«Are you aware of the problems with your memory?»'

«Yes.»

«Language problems?»

«Yes.»

«If you should meet a girl – what sort of girl should it be, if it's going to work out?»

Tobias is silent. He wants me to speak for him. He doesn't say so, but I feel it.

«How would it be if you met a girl with the same problems that you have: memory problems and aphasia?»

I wonder a little, aloud, that perhaps it would be a good thing. But then say that maybe it would be a little difficult. «How would you two communicate? Who would find the right words?»

Tobias doesn't want to learn picto-, sign-, or symbol-communication. Perhaps because, deep inside, he knows that he cannot learn them. Letters form words and are kind of sound signs. He has forgotten sound signs. What is there that says that he can learn image-signs instead? Symbols are symbols, and his memory is damaged. Learning communication symbols is difficult, no matter which senses are involved. Spontaneously, he decides to emphasise certain words by using his hand, drawing pictures in the air. He doesn't draw symbols; he draws real details from memories of the place or person that he connects with the event that he wants to describe. Unfortunately, most people find it difficult to decipher the drawings if they were not there just then.

I continue talking about how Tobias is living in a rich, inner world, lacking words, and in need of someone who can guess what he wants to say.

Tobias listens, thinks, but doesn't know.

«You really know that you lack memory and words?»

«Yes.»

«It's painful?»

«Yes.»

«But good, too,» I say. «That you are aware of it.»

I describe how it would be if he was unaware of his limitations, which he is when he is psychotic and goes into an omnipotent, fantasy world, where there are no limits, not even those that limit us mere mortals.

«You remember everything, and have all the words... and we know and see that you lack both memory and words. We would be miles from each other. When you are aware, you and I see the same Tobias, we are close. You can accept help, and can take part in almost everything.»

«Hmm.»

SEEING THINGS FROM THE BRIGHTER SIDE

It can't be taught to others. Many people ask me about my ability to manage with my loss. The easiest, in fact deceptively easy and not at all easy way is that I refrain from managing. I use no «tools», I don't think positively, I don't search for a meaning in the meaningless. No, I am. I feel pain when it comes, I give up, I give in, I cry until the tears finish, and I don't dislike myself. That is the key. I can feel all this without shame, without thinking that sorrow is bad or that I am weak.

People seem to be mostly afraid of weakness. Weakness is associated with being at a disadvantage, inferiority and contempt. Such fears are based upon the fear of the contempt of others and one's own self-contempt. Self-contempt is not genetic. Has anyone seen an infant feeling self-contempt when it fulfils its needs of physical and emotional care? How could they? It is a good question, how anyone could know, how it could be seen, how one knows what an infant feels. Psychological theories about what babies feel are partly based upon observations of their behaviour and facial expressions, and partly on patients' memories of their early years, re-experienced in psychotherapy or body-focused methods together with breathing exercises, music, etcetera. As an expert in hypnosis, I see these as methods used to achieve a state of trance. In a state of trance, or an altered state of consciousness as it is more generally termed, one reaches deeper levels, «the sub- or unconscious», the so-called implicit memories. These kinds of experiences often lack words, they are perceived as bodily sensations and can be translated into words by the person experiencing it or by the therapist, if help is needed. What I, thus, claim is that, using my own and others' long clinical experience, we believe that we can guess fairly well just how infancy is experienced.

To get back to the subject of self-contempt; when does this make its first appearance in a person's life? It appears when the infant starts to separate itself from its closest caregiver, when it realizes that the evident twosomeness with the mother (or father if he is closest) suddenly disappears, and when frustrations such as too long periods of solitude cause anxiety. This anxiety is a form of fear of death, and is sometimes called annihilation anxiety. If the caregivers that are closest don't manage to cope sufficiently and with a warm, loving empathy, with the child's terrible feelings, its feelings of abandonment will be overwhelming. To get secure closeness is a basic innate need, just as important as food and warmth. Infants are self-centred. Everything starts with them.

The self-centredness of childhood is probably a necessary base from which a feeling of identity can grow. However, it also means that anxiety or neglect that they are exposed to will be felt by the infant as being self-inflicted. When I use the word «self-inflicted» I base this on the assumption that the infant has a sense of self from an early age. It is very difficult to say how early. Merely behavioural observations cannot assess psychological phenomena such as an inner sense of self. The psychologists who speak about early sense of self, base the assumption upon the psychotherapy of children, adolescents and adults who can describe that they remember how they felt. Memories, however, can never be quite free from time-contamination. More mature interpretations of recollections from childhood can infiltrate these childhood memories, so that the intent, meaning and values are attributed to what they think they remember. However, one can assume that the flashbacks, in which specific locations and contexts occur together with a specific feeling, are probably consistent with how it was actually experienced in the initial situation. But, if the person remembering the images and emotions from early childhood, also says «I was not desired,» you might wonder whether such an interpretation derives from later experiences and conclusions, or whether, as very small children, they can really, firstly, experience the wordless, bodily sensation of being a separate person, and secondly, also experience being unwanted or rejected by an external person. I would rather claim that we just don't know. But I believe that the narrations I have been told by patients who regress (go back in age) to early childhood experiences, are very advanced as well as being so physically perceived that they seem genuine and not a product of mere fantasy.

Neglected children, thus, feel that they are not worthy of being loved. «I am basically faulty, I am disgusting, it's in my blood,» are examples of what I can hear from my patients who have lacked loving care early in life.

Self-disgust leads to a feeling of shame. I do not mean the mature shame that we commonly call a bad conscience or feelings of shame that all of us can feel when we have hurt or abused someone and badly wish it to be un-done. The feeling of shame that can cause self-disgust is experienced as a conviction that deep inside, you are not acceptable as you are. Shame, unlike guilt, cannot be repaired through an act of reparation and atonement. Shame is not the result of a number of small mistakes that one can learn from. This feeling of shame must be concealed, because if it becomes visible one will be revealed as being useless. It is a feeling of being totally rejected that causes shame. The feeling of being rejected is associated with not being good enough in any shape of form, other than that of a deviant. To be a deviant, and different, can mean that one finds oneself on the outside, as is often the case in fundamentalist cultures. When one is excluded from human society, one's soul almost dies. Some children feel panic, others become restless, while others become apathetic, especially if the rejection is sustained.

As long as we feel accepted as we are, which is a feeling founded in belonging and fellowship, then we can cope with all kinds of feelings, including psychological pain. No matter how it is expressed, when someone is suffering there is only one cure. SSRI, Selective serotonin reuptake inhibitor; the modern anti-depressive medicine. No, just joking! If one is allowed to joke about matters like this. No, one oughtn't to. But I did. Because this is too often the remedy suggested by the doctor. When pain has entrenched itself. It appears like a major depression according to modern psychiatric diagnostics. When I was a young psychologist, this was called Endogenous Depression. Endogenous means arising from inside the organism. In other words, it is a depression that is not caused by external factors. The assumption is that these depressions are created by the brain for no other reason than congenital constitution. When the diagnosis was changed to major depression, the division into internal and external was dropped since the «stress/vulnerability» model had become widely accepted. This means that most psychiatrists these days acknowledge the importance of surroundings for the development of depression, even those depressions that are emanating from a constitutional propensity, or vulnerability. One can say that we are born more or less vulnerable, more or less robust, and more or less thick-skinned. A vulnerable person that is part of a fellowship, who feels loved and is seen, and who is allowed to express her sensitivity will most probably never develop any form of mental illness or disorder and thus avoid having her brain chemistry modified by medicines, other than in extreme cases or in the case of a brain injury that disturbs the brain's ability to regulate its chemical and hormonal balance.

Johan Beck-Friis (2005) writes that depression differs from normal sadness, depression, withdrawal and sorrow, and he uses an illustrative term for the difference, namely, depression's loss of self-respect. We can also see this with people who have an acquired brain injury. Beck-Friis' book about depression as lost self-respect can be recommended as an aid for neuro-psychologists and psychiatrists who must diagnose people with acquired brain injury, with or without aphasia. The most common diagnostic assessments and manuals are quite impossible to use for this group of patients, since most symptoms can be a direct result of brain damage and mental trauma. It is impossible to know whether the cause is a lesion or damaged self-esteem, but the latter should be taken into greater account than is the case at the moment. The symptoms named for the various depression diagnoses (dysthymia, major depression and melancholia), are: decreased happiness, sadness, early awakening, a change in appetite, a change in weight, sleep disturbance, lack of energy, fatigue, quietness, withdrawal, tearfulness, despair, etcetera. I won't continue this list as it is obvious to me that it is meaningless to just list symptoms! What counts is dignity and reciprocity. These are found in relationships where one is regarded as being important. With an acquired brain injury, one has lost the significance one once had, with a loss of self-esteem as a result. Beck-Friis writes on page 207: «If one considers depression as an expression of lost self-esteem, no matter the grade or nature of the depression, respect for the depressed person's dignity must be a key element in any form of treatment.» Later on in the book he discusses medication and psychotherapy. His view is that medication is necessary with deep depression and that «only light or medium depressions are suitable for psychotherapy alone».

As can be seen from what I have already written, I have realised the need for medication during an acute state of manic psychosis. However, I am more optimistic than Beck-Friis and many other psychiatrists about the possibilities of treating even the deepest of depressions, those where self-esteem is lacking, through psychotherapy. If I understand his book correctly, Beck-Friis believes that the difference between a medium depression and a deep one is the resignation, and the feeling of being worthless. This correlates well neurologically in the form of deranged, retarded and agitated biochemical processes that, from a biological viewpoint, must be stopped in order to avoid fastening in a vicious circle and becoming chronic. One intervenes through medication. This seems logical, but from experience I know that deep depression can be interrupted with dialogue and deep relaxation / hypnosis with harmonizing suggestions, especially as all I say and do is aimed at helping the patient regain her self-esteem. Surprisingly often, maybe after only a few weeks, the patient surfaces from her deep depression when she both knows and, more importantly, feels that her despair has an intelligible and logical cause that can be discussed.

Self-respect is bound to be deeply impaired when people are depressed owing to an unbearable alienation, the loss of brain functions, and participation in society.

Many of us psychologists and psychotherapists have solid, and deep understanding about existential problems, crisis-management and grief, as well as how the patients' individual resources can be stimulated using empathetic dialogue and creative forms of therapy.

Regardless of how well we listen to someone in pain, we can only help in a profound way if we can see the human need *for love, community and belonging.*

These needs are strong. They have a dynamic power that can release a lust for life if it is encouraged. Lust for life drives and leads us forward. The only thing that can stop us is if we feel unwanted, that our grief is too heavy for others to witness. Yes, witness. I don't write carry, since no one can carry someone else's psychological burden. We can feel some relief for a while when we share our grief, *as if* someone is carrying it for us. But they don't really. The best help with grief is when someone is by our side, listening, accepting and is just there. That is sufficient.

I can contribute to the joy in other people, but I cannot request those I am helping to feel happiness. Under no circumstances can I tell my clients how to feel or think other than in the form of seeding ideas that can help them forward, seeds that if the conditions are favourable, might grow and put down roots. Happiness is a state of mind that lasts as long as it lasts. When you see a really happy child, her feeling of happiness comes spontaneously from within. It is either as a reaction to something someone says or does, or some external event that awakens the child's imagination. The laughter comes from inside, as a reaction to something.

Therefore, if you want to help someone in a state of distress and/or make someone happy, you can only contribute to the creation of an atmosphere that might allow the other to come into a state of mind where happiness is a possibility.

This is what I do – as a mother, a wife, a grandmother and a psychotherapist.

One of my teachers at the University said that therapists seduce their patients to desire. It is not sexual seduction, unless one views everything desirable as being basically sexual, as is the case in obsolete Freudian terminology.

Parents seduce their children to desire, play and learning. Desire comes first, and it promotes growth, communication and mutual happiness. The atmosphere of such experience facilitates open-minded receptivity and new learning. It is at moments like these one can feel hope for the future with less mourning.

(Written 20th June 2010)

REFERENCE

Beck-Friis, J. (2005) *När Orfeus vände sig om. En bok om depression som förlorad självaktning.* Natur & Kultur.

Tobias

AN ABRUPT END

It is the 27th of June, the Sunday day after Midsummer Day. On Midsummer Day, I had a fall and scraped the inside of my wrist. Tobias looks at the cut and then looks at me, kindly, enquiringly, and asks about it. I don't grasp exactly what he says, as I am used to the fact that his tone of voice and facial expressions supplements his few words, thus letting me «hear» sentences. Perhaps all he says is «What?» I don't know. What he does say with this multi-faceted expression is: «Have you really fallen down? It looks more like you have cut it yourself, that cut looks like a suicide cut, though it's hard to believe it, but I'm asking anyway.»

Those who are familiar with Tobias know that he can express himself as well as this, with the help of a couple of words, which are of a lesser importance. They will be what he finds in his brain's meagre vocabulary.

The whole Midsummer weekend holiday was lovely. Tobias is feeling better than ever after his accident 1996. He is considerate, and aware of his injury. Earlier, I discussed the reasons why it is positive that he is conscious about his injury, but I will do it again. It is positive and can help him in his development now that he no longer needs to be ashamed of the effects of his injury other than when meeting new people or when he meets young attractive women. He takes an ever greater responsibility for his limitations by explaining his strange behaviour and is increasingly often able to refer to his injury. Take this weekend as an example, when he finds his little nephew difficult and demanding, he points to the left part of his head, letting me know that he is intolerant to the screaming and intensity of the child because of his injury.

246

On Sunday evening we part at Saltholmen. We have had a wonderful afternoon in the sun on the lawn, and Tobias has enjoyed it, resting in a hanging chair under the whitebeam tree. We've eaten salmon and then ice-cream, leftovers from the Midsummer celebrations. The two of us have been alone a couple of hours after his friend Fredrik and family, brother Mårten and family, and papa Tore have all gone back to town. Tobias and I took a later boat, as Tobias was going home. He wanted to visit café Zenit, then watch TV and have a week at home before going off on a week's visit to a rehabilitation retreat. He is very harmonious.

It is Monday, the 28th of June. This morning, I am supervising a health and care team. For this reason, my mobile telephone is switched off.

When I finally turn it back on I see that I have a message. I listen and hear Tobias' assistant say: «Hello, Susanna, ring me immediately you hear this.» Oh dear, he's never expressed himself like that before. Whenever the assistants have needed my help with Tobias it has sounded like this: « ... phone when you've got a minute», or if it has been very urgent «call as soon as you can», implying that if I have something very important to do then the call can wait. This, however, is different. I have time to think that it may be that Tobias has become acutely and unexpectedly psychotic, that he has behaved violently, that the police have been called in, perhaps, or, in the worst case, that he has injured himself. I take it that something has happened that the assistants can't cope with without my direct help. I phone.

«Has anyone else spoken to you?» asks Anders.

«No.»

«Well ... it's Tobias ... he's dead.»

My brain registers the words as being true directly, but my emotions don't react yet, of course. He couldn't have said it better, simpler or clearer. I appreciate his direct approach.

«Where are you?» I ask. «We are in Tobias' flat.» I say: «I'm on my way, I'll cycle directly». «Good,» answers Anders.

I react while I'm cycling. I cry the whole of the 15 minutes it takes to cycle from the city to Tobias' home.

I enter the flat. My tears cut off automatically, I am about to meet a totally new situation for me. A doctor approaches and shakes my hand. Rather awkwardly. I don't know who she is; I don't know that she is a doctor. She says: «Nina ...» I can't hear the rest of the name, she speaks unclearly or too quickly. «Aha, the doctor?» «Yes. It's like this; I must ask ... it's customary that one performs a post-mortem when someone is found dead. Is this acceptable?» «Yes, yes, of course.» She then goes. Maybe she says: «my condolences» or something afterwards, I can't hear her.

I go up to Tobias' body. Touch him, despite the fact that the sight is horrible. He is surrounded by black. Like soot. Blue-black in parts of his face, chest and shoulders and black flecks on his body. The sheets, eiderdown and pillows are also flecked in black. There are black spots on the wallpaper. My first thoughts are «has some burglar been in and killed him? My son! No one may touch him!» Then I suddenly realise that he has died of an epileptic seizure.

Dead blood is black, apparently. Either that or light red, I have learned. Why? My guess: No oxygen, no oxidation, no rust-brown.

He is slightly sunburned but dead. This I can see. A dead body, but it is still Tobias. I recognise Tobias after an epileptic seizure. One foot slightly curved, the cramp hadn't loosened totally. His right hand clenched. But his face is relaxed. He can't have died during the first cramps, but when the worst was over.

Tobias!

He still feels warm. Strange, the attacks usually occur between 01.00 and 02.00 at the latest. Maybe he got 40 degrees fever during the attack and it can thus take time to cool down. It's just a body, his body; this is what he looked like. I can see that his right hand is clenched, as I've seen it after an attack. Now I notice that it is his left foot that is slightly bent. It is usually the right foot that is affected during a seizure, but this seizure must have strongly involved both halves of the brain. I wonder about all this blood. He usually bites himself in the tongue or the cheek, bleed a little and basically have a smelly blood-mixed saliva and phlegm mixture from his throat, but never so much pure blood.

Time to leave these thoughts, the dead body and go out to the others.

Sitting out on the lawn, John is heartbroken. He can't escape his shock, the image of Tobias' dead face. He was expectant this morning, happy to be Tobias' assistant this summer and everyone was looking forward to a lovely summer. It was John's first day as Tobias' assistant. John, who has known Tobias since 1997. John, who has been his film and painting teacher, magazine editing teacher, and travel companion during the summers between 1997 – 2006, as well as now, after a longer pause, his art mentor and soon his assistant this summer.

Anders was involved, too, this morning, introducing John to his new job. Tobias lay quietly in his bed; they thought he was asleep. Anders went off on an errand. John made a cup of coffee in the kitchen and waited for Tobias to wake up. He made small noises with the cups and saucers. At ten o'clock John went in and lifted Tobias' eiderdown.

He met a dead face, a dead body and no smiling Tobias. Shock. Blood. John started CPR (Cardiopulmonary resuscitation). He hadn't realised that Tobias was already dead. He phoned 112 and he phoned Anders. The doctor who was to confirm death turned up. They phoned Mårten who came together with his wife, Pia. Pia tried to get hold of me at work, but I didn't answer. Pia then went to my studio but I was at the workplace of those I was supervising. Pia or Mårten reached Tore who broke off work and returned to Göteborg.

Terrible, terrible.

John took the blow, I wish it had been me; I was at least prepared for it.[16] I have such a strong imagination, I always expect the worst, not because I'm a pessimist, though, because I'm not. I'm an optimist. An optimist that always expects the best, but is always prepared for everything, always, just so that I won't be shocked, and be able to handle everything that comes my way and still keep my optimism in the sense of: we'll manage – life is for us – let's just manage this first. Even this.

It stinks. Maybe of faeces. Strangely, it didn't smell this morning at eight o'clock when the assistants arrived.

Tore phones me. «You don't have to come home now if you're busy,» I say. Oh yes, what am I thinking, of course he wants to come home. On the train, Tore goes through his address book and phones to friends and relations to tell them. Anders Grahn, Mårten and I phone to all the other assistants, friends and authorities. John is in pain. I don't envy him, what a sight ...

Mårten goes to Café Zenit and buys us all lunch. Tobias' favourite; toast and salad with coffee. I ask Mårten's wife, Pia, to go and buy plastic sacks so that we can put away the bloody sheets, pillows and eiderdown. We go down to the refuse bins with two sacks and a mattress, of highest quality. But they smell, and they can't be cleaned. I take a look around, and decide everything else can wait till tomorrow.

---

16 John, the translator's, comment: Susanna, I think in the circumstances that it was fine that I took that blow. I was the least involved with Tobias day to day and yet knew him so well. Someone had to be there, and I was the one who could probably cope in the long run. I felt many times that it was my fault but at the same time, rationally, I knew that this was definitely not so.

It is six o'clock in the evening and I cycle in to my gym where I run for 30 minutes on the running belt, writing poems in my head. They are beautiful but I can't remember them afterwards. By eight o'clock I am with Tore in our favourite restaurant.

I don't think I fall asleep before 3 in the morning. Tore and I had gone to bed at 9 in the evening. There is nothing we can do. I usually fall asleep easily, but not tonight. The last time I had difficulty sleeping was when Tobias was psychotic and manic, but this was almost a year ago. I pray to a higher Being, who, for simplicity, I shall call God, for help to relax mentally so that I can sleep. This has no effect. I ask Tobias for help. A wave of peace descends upon me then, and I can relax, but not sleep. In the early hours of the morning, I get a pain in the left side of my brain, just where Tobias' injury was. I also have a slight pain on the top of my right foot, just where Tobias usually has the worst cramp during a seizure.

I think about all the wonderful things we have done, his beautiful eyes, beautiful voice, beautiful gestures, and his beautiful posture. I think of the pleasant smell of him, that fortunately is already erasing the smell of death.

The day after tomorrow, the 30th of June, the undertakers will be coming.

I think about the fact that I have been through mourning once before, 14 years ago. We mourned the Tobias that one time was. We mourned, we worried, and we were in a state of crisis. This is different.

The funeral is planned. We do it quickly. Our first thoughts are about a church. Then it struck us that we can choose a civic ceremony. What would Tobias have wanted? Mårten: Tobias went to the end-of-school ceremony in Vasa church when he was at junior school. Me: Yes, but he got up and went out when a priest, like an old-fashioned preacher, urged the children to have a good holiday but «not without Jesus; you can do all sorts of things, but not without Jesus». There were lots of things Tobias didn't like about the church. He liked

Brännö, though. The ceremony ought to take place on Brännö. In Brännö church?

The undertaker: Was Tobias' attitude rather scientific? Perhaps the restaurant's glass-house on Brännö, which is as big as a church, could be hired?

I immediately imagine the beautiful glass-house, full of flowers and atmosphere. It is also better than a church would be, as regards accessibility for people with disabilities. His friends in wheelchairs would have no problems and Tobias would have liked this.

But, church or civic? A priest? Tore: It is so very profane without a priest.

We are really bewildered and start discussing what Tobias would have wanted. We can't come to any agreement. I decide to send the question to Tobias, as I am the one who can «hear» his answer. There's a big risk that I'll hear an answer that is in my favour, one would think. No one in the family believes any of this at this point. Tobias' answer comes quickly and surprisingly. Tobias: Mama. Don't ask me. I'll go along with all your alternatives. The funeral isn't mine, it's yours, and it's for all of you. Do what feels right for yourselves!

We finally make a decision. Tore has his mind on a certain priest, Lars, who we all know and who met Tobias as a child. We all like him. Mårten wants a cantor who is also a very talented pianist, Thomas Gustavsson, conductor of the «New Tide Orquesta». We all know who he is and appreciate his music. Tobias' closest friends these last 13 years, Micke and Lena need accessibility and the ability to come in the taxi. His girlfriend and friend, Carola, will be coming all the way from Hässleholm for the funeral. This means that being in Göteborg is an advantage as regards accessibility. We all agree that Tobias would have preferred an imposing place for his ceremony. He was living in the parish of Masthugget, so why not Masthugget church?

I just used the word «ceremony». This is a gentle way of letting my readers approach the use of the word I want to use: Celebration. I can't feel that Tobias' funeral should be dark and sad. This is not Tobias. This is our last celebration with Tobias. Celebration, not funeral.

People phone, send us texts, emails and flowers. White, pink, yellow, green and blue. No one dares to send red flowers, even though I imagine that many people think that red is what would have suited Tobias best.

Tuesday is a day of torture for Tore. He feels such a desperate emptiness that he doesn't dare to be alone. As I plan to stay in town, he does the same. He absolutely doesn't want to be alone on Brännö. I am the kind of person who is strongest alone, so I didn't share his distress. But I am very, very sad.

Wednesday is a strange day. Strange and wonderful. I have read about widows who «see» their late husbands. My mother-in-law saw her husband in the bedroom doorway after his death and I hope to see Tobias in some form. I imagine that he will show up at Brännö where he felt so at home. I imagine his shape will turn up in the house, in his room. I am cycling from town to Saltholmen. I have been cycling for twenty minutes when, 2 kilometres from Saltholmen, I feel a warmth and happiness in my body. I can feel Tobias' presence, but not beside me, as I had expected, but within me. Oh, what a surprise! He is inside my body, he fills me!

I am filled with an indescribable thankfulness. It is eleven o'clock.

I am on Brännö and the time is half past one in the afternoon. Tore phones.

He says:

«You don't have to be worried about me anymore. I no longer feel empty. Tobias turned up, inside me! I am calm. It feels good.»

Sunday

Mårten phones about the funeral coffee. We discuss what limits we should draw up as regards taking part in the memorial service after church. Can everybody take part? I tell Mårten that we should set a limit and that maybe we will have to say no to those who I think are outside that limit. I put the phone down.

What do you want, Tobias? I ask. His answer comes immediately: The memory service should be for everyone who wants to come. We may not exclude anyone! I phone to Mårten and tell him what Tobias wants.

It's called serendipity. A happy chance. I take a book out of the bookcase. It's a book that I read a few weeks ago, but which I had put aside because its contents hadn't really interested me. The language was beautiful, but this was the only reason that I had continued to read it. But I never read it to the end. I had started another book to read on the boat, the tram, or the bus, instead. I have no idea really why I started this book again, but I did. I couldn't really remember what it was about more than that the main character had rented a cottage by a lake in the middle of Sweden and was trying to write about his life. I re-read a few chapters to remind myself about what the author is telling us. My God, all the time he has been writing about the death of his daughter and I had totally let this pass me by. It's maybe not so strange. I am a psychotherapist; I listen to people's life stories hour after hour. There is a limit to how many human destinies I can be absorbed by, so in my spare time I tend to avoid the life stories of, for me, unknown people. This, however, is different. I have also lost a child. The discussions towards the end of the book are intimate, human, and fallible, the limits of verbal language are aptly laid bare and the polarities between solitude and fellowship and superbly drawn.

It is a really special chance that led me to choose this book right now. Another coincidence is that I have been thinking intensively for a few days about one of our relatives and been hoping that she calls off attending the funeral. This relative and my mother, Tobias' grandmother, had a conflict after an earlier death in the family, and they haven't made up since then. My mother is very sensitive, and I want the funeral service to have an undisturbed atmosphere, but at the same time I can't just ask someone not to come, and Tobias wouldn't want it either. Then the relative phones to say that while meditating she came to understand that grandmother is suffering deep sorrow and that her own presence would cause unnecessary distress so she will not come. I receive this insight thankfully and express my appreciation. Serendipity; my inner wish came true.

A patient comes for her second visit. Her problem is addiction. I start the session by telling her of my doubts; is she as honest as she seems to be? Is she fooling herself like so many other addicts? How hard is it going to be to try to help her? When I tell her of my misgivings she replies that she has had similar thoughts about me. My attitude seems to be so good, but maybe I am fooling her. The professionals that have gathered to help her have perhaps conspired to trick her, to lead her into a trap. Besides, she has doubts about her own ability to free herself from drugs; it is hard for her to imagine a drug-free identity for herself. Two souls with the same thought. Serendipity.

Now that nine days have passed since Tobias died, I am amazed about how I am adapting myself to his death. As a friend said: «I'll say like Tobias would, 'Fucking shame!' »

Quite right. That's what he would have said. Our Tobias. I can smile. I can adjust to this. It's a question of my temperament and personality. Some people have difficulties in adapting to new situations. I am extraordinarily good at assimilating, learning and adapting to situations, at the price of having a rather good memory. Agreements, practical decisions and promises are final. For instance, should my husband change his mind about something which also includes me actively, I have to make a huge effort to re-think and act as if the earlier decision hadn't been made. Learning new things is easy, erasing previously learnt lessons is more difficult. This makes me think about ageing. They say that elderly are not good at learning new things: You can't teach old dog new tricks. But maybe it's because older people have already learned most things at least once before, but with different concepts. A lot of old knowledge is marketed in new packages, influenced by modern contexts and values; maybe we are not as motivated to learn the same thing in a new variation, and with more modern and less analyzed normative assumptions? The best we can do then is to analyze the innovation, analyze what is novel about it, and compare, and then make a conscious choice of which edition we prefer.

I adapt to Tobias' death at a fantastic rate. One day of tears, one day of desperate emptiness, several days of an intensive presence with Tobias inside me and endless dreaming about his funeral, etcetera. My time awake is now filled with memories, memories and more memories ... if nothing else is demanding my focus of attention. Tobias has also stopped visiting my dreams. Last night, eleven days after his death, I dreamt about my work, in new situations where I help unknown, disabled adults. During the daytime, though, I carry with me all the habits that he created with his special needs. I find myself planning next year's work and congresses with the same restraints as earlier, «so long as Tobias agrees». Tobias' needs have naturally come first. Not now, though. I have difficulty coping with this new freedom. Freedom feels positive. Loss is negative. I must reconcile this, somehow. I will perhaps go in therapy in the autumn. It doesn't feel like I need an advisor; it must be a therapist with an existential psychodynamic understanding that I have my own answers, I don't need homework, good advice or strategic questions about how I should cope. I can feel it so clearly! We are surely going to need a year of mourning, but thank God we didn't lose Tobias in 1996, when he was strong, healthy and with a normal future ahead of him. Instead, we have been endowed with 14 years of rich, instructive and incredibly loving struggle in harmony with Tobias' infinite patience and his infinite gratitude for our patient collaboration with him.

At Tobias' funeral I said this, more or less:

«I will stand up now and hold a speech. It feels very good to do this as I know that Tobias liked when I spoke publicly about disability and care, with Tobias as an example. He sat in the audience a few times or participated on the stage, and he appreciated it. It feels as if he is taking part now, too. Not there, in the coffin, he's not there. No, I can see him sitting in one of the empty benches at the front. His presence is tangible.

There are no words for this sorrow. This is what people say to us, because what can one say? Whatever one says feels trivial. 'If silence could speak' is a well-known phrase. I turn to you, now, Tobias, and instead of talking about you I will talk to you. Your silence could in fact speak.

You spoke with your eyes, your beautiful, warm, grey-blue eyes. They were cold black, though, when you were disappointed about your situation. Or angry. There was no doubt about what you were feeling.

You spoke with your left hand, your slender, sensitive, soft hand when you wanted to hug. Your first sign after waking from the anaesthesia, 14 years ago, before you could use your vocal chords and before we knew if you could express yourself at all was; thumbs up. Later, you used to pat Tore's bald spot as a sign of affection. In answer to the eternal question of how you were getting on you would show you hand bent slightly upwards 'better and better'. Or you might want to throw a punch in despair over your inferiority.

You spoke through your fragrance, that harmonic, sensual smell of almonds that you exuded. Or the bad odour of your breath when you were anxious and restless.

You spoke with your tone of voice, indicating request, surprise, wonder, tenacity, self-assertion, humility, kindness and consideration.

You spoke with your charisma that could be the most present, spiritual, patient, calm and divine energy that I, we, have ever experienced.

All this silent communication remains, within us, and is probably even stronger than when you were with us in body. It feels like you have given us a gift to care for, so that we can continue to contribute to the good in life, each of us in our own way according to our abilities, wherever we are in the future.

Thanks Tobias.»

I was alone in the building later that day, after the funeral celebration with cappuccino, buffet, joyful speeches and music. All the guests and even those people who had stayed behind to help clear up had gone. Suddenly, I felt a strong body odour. My own armpits only exuded a pale smell of deodorant and nothing else. No one else was there. I then heard Tobias say within me: «You spoke about all those smells I had in your speech but you forgot to name my arm sweat that you were always on at me about!»

Tobias meant a lot to many people. His achievement was to teach us humility in the face of life's twists and turns, to cope with adversity by making the best of every now. The best we could give Tobias was love, joy, humour, thorough honesty and patience. He gave us all this when he could, and when he couldn't we gave it all back to him. Together, we created a good circle.

Now, seven weeks after his death, I feel filled of everything he gave me. I am more inspired that ever in my work as a psychologist and a psychotherapist. I trust my intuition more than ever (it is most probably freer from worries of my own) and I still feel Tobias presence. Less as a personal Tobias and more as a harmonic force. I suspect that our year of morning will be a mixed one; light and dark will come and go, but the light will dominate.

I didn't read out a certain poem that I had planned for the funeral celebration. I had received a mail from an English colleague containing a poem from the late 19th century. I had never seen this poem before. It expressed my feelings about death. I had translated it for the service. However, a few days before Tobias' funeral, I attended another funeral. The funeral of my daughter-in-law's father. Suddenly, Pia, my daughter-in-law, brought forth exactly the same poem to read at the service, a poem that was totally unknown to her before. She didn't know that I had just received the same poem from my colleague. Serendipity and synchronicity. It feels good that the same poem had found its way to us. Pia's is a Swedish translation that I didn't know existed. Luckily, since I prefer my own translation.

I would like to conclude by paying tribute to Tobias. Firstly, via a mail that I received from a personal assistant, since this mail shows some of Tobias' greatness. This greatness is all the more impressive when one thinks of how damaged his brain was. The soul couldn't be damaged, as I see now.

Well, after the funeral, I received this mail from the former assistant, Calle, who had finished working with Tobias half a year earlier. He had attended the funeral.

«Tobias and I were hardly an inseparable pair. Had I met him before his accident I doubt whether we would have become close friends. Not properly, anyway.

I got to know the disabled Tobias. It was a job, I needed a job just then. It turned out to be more than that. I have often thought how lucky he was. Lucky that he was your son. That he was Mårten's brother. Unconditional love and strength that I can't even begin to understand.

My strongest memory:

It was one of those days when I was feeling not at all well. This was right before the breakdown that caused me to stop working. Right from the outset this day, I was uncertain whether I could cope with assisting and understanding. Whether I would have any patience.

I hadn't needed to worry. It turned out to be one of the best days I had with Tobias. Seen from my own egoistical viewpoint that is.

That day, Tobias saw me as he had never done before. We had no misunderstandings, which was unusual in itself.

I am certain that he understood that I was feeling badly that day. Even though I didn't say anything, I am certain that he knew something was badly wrong.

He was very kind, and patient about how I was. He gave me calming and comforting looks. Rather like 'It's okay', 'things are going to work out', 'it doesn't matter' … this sort of thing.

It's hard to explain, but something like that.

Nobody that day could have made me feel better. No one. Not you. Not myself. Not my best friend or my partner. When I left Tobias that day, it felt as if I could breathe again. I honestly felt as if I could fly.

Fantastic and inexplicable, isn't it?

I shall never forget it.

/Calle»

The poem I mentioned above, the poem that both Pia and I found at the time of the deaths of our loved ones, describes the feelings about death that I have had these last few years. I hope it can be an inspiration.

«DEATH is nothing at all. I have only slipped away into the next room. I am I and you are you. Whatever we were to each other, that we still are.

Call me by my old familiar name; speak to me in the easy way which you always used. Put no difference into your tone, wear no forced air of solemnity or sorrow.

Laugh as we always laughed at the little jokes we enjoyed together. Play, smile, think of me. Pray for me. Let my name be ever the household word that it always was, let it be spoken without effort, without the trace of a shadow on it.

Life means all that it ever meant. It is the same as it ever was; there is unbroken continuity. Why should I be out of mind because I am out of sight?

I am waiting for you, for an interval somewhere very near, just round the corner.

All is well.»

Henry Scott Holland 1847-1918 Canon of St Pauls Cathedral

Tobias adds: «Better and better.»

24th of August

It strikes me that I will never, ever, see Tobias coming towards me with his warm, grateful, appreciative smile!

Light and dark interwoven.

16th of December

I know that I can see Tobias whenever I want to. Light is stronger than darkness.

04450948